1-7-89
2⁵⁰

From the Collection of the Cincinnati Art Museum

ART OF THE FIRST AMERICANS

Copyright Cincinnati Art Museum, 1976
Eden Park, Cincinnati, Ohio 45202

This project is supported by a grant from the National Endowment for the Arts, a Federal agency in Washington, D.C. Matching funds were provided by generous grants from Farny R. and Grace K. Wurlitzer Foundation, from Summerfair, Inc. and from Mrs. Paul W. Christensen.

Foreword

367

Row upon row of exhibition cases crowded with baskets and stone implements, clay bowls and decorated hides offered the only picture of the American Indian most of us would ever see in the decades immediately following the white man's establishment in this vast land. In lines like soldiers, what did these exhibited objects crafted by Hopi, Sioux and Chilkat tell us? They were collected as works of art, as curiosities, or relics of history. In collecting what the American Indian crafted, museums somewhat unintentionally preserved a great artistic heritage while concentrating on the archaeological or curious aspects of the Indians' craftsmanship. Museums have a proud record of collecting, preserving, and exhibiting American Indian art, midst an otherwise sad record of treatment and recognition of these native Americans. So the past exhibitions of Indian art and objects in American museums, although ringing dimly-lighted galleries as specimens in a rock collection might be displayed, established appreciation and wonderment that historians, anthropologists, scientists, and art historians are more recently beginning to grasp. Art historical interpretation and archaeological investigation have elevated the world's understanding of American Indian art for scholar and student. Art museums proudly display and collect these objects with full attention to their artistic, visual qualities.

One of the first assignments I gave myself in the weeks after I arrived as Director of the Cincinnati Art Museum was to explore the network of storage rooms that held the Museum's reserve of unexhibited works of art. This task rewarded me with many surprises, mostly pleasant ones, including the inspection of a vast array (about 50,000 accessioned objects) of American Indian pottery, beadwork, decorated hides, wooden masks, stone pipes—a collection within a collection, an iceberg-like group of objects that is the Museum's largest family of related works of art. This collection was already being studied by two of our curators, Carolyn R. Shine and Mary L. Meyer. Plans for the collection's cataloguing and exhibiting were initiated in the basement storerooms when I first saw these beautiful objects. The results of countless hours of research, study, planning, and labor are evidenced in the catalogue and display, *Art of the First Americans.*

Art of the First Americans is above all a tribute to the Indian of the North American Continent. It serves also as the Cincinnati Art Museum's major salute to our nation's Bicentennial (1776-1976). It resurrects in ways never seen in Cincinnati or published before, these artistic resources of our Museum. It acknowledges the past collectors, donors, and curators for their interest in the artifacts the Museum possesses merely as guardians. *Art of the First Americans* is a selection of the finest, rarest, and most attractive examples of American Indian art in the Cincinnati Art Museum's collection. That the exhibition is drawn exclusively from our own holdings and does not depend on borrowed objects reaffirms the Museum's collecting strengths built up over many decades. It also emphasizes a trend among American museums to focus on their own collections that often were neglected in favor of transient, temporary shows.

Supporting financial grants are acknowledged with gratitude from the National Endowment for the Arts, the Farny R. and Grace K. Wurlitzer Foundation, Cincinnati's Summerfair, Inc., and The Squash Blossom. A generous gift from Mrs. Paul W. Christensen permitted the acquisition of equipment for the Conservation Dept. to assist in the cleaning of Indian materials.

The Cincinnati Art Museum commissioned Dr. James B. Griffin, Department of Anthropology, University of Michigan, and Dr. Beth Dillingham, Department of Anthropology, University of Cincinnati, for scholarly assistance in studying, classifying, and interpreting the Museum's collection of American Indian art. In addition, they wrote essays for the catalogue to illuminate the material and place our collection in a broader context.

Dr. Gustav Carlson, Head of the Department of Anthropology of the University of Cincinnati, should also be thanked, somewhat after the fact, for the labors he performed some thirty-five years ago in sorting and recording the Indian material in the Museum, most of it not previously inventoried. Dr. Kent Vickery assisted generously with advice and identification.

Dr. Richard Davis, Museum of Natural History, Cincinnati, helped initiate the use of the Airbrasive machine for cleaning Indian objects and Dr. Kenneth Caster of the University of

Cincinnati's Geology Department not only arranged this interinstitutional service, but also gave considerable time to helping identify the rock from which so many of the archaeological objects were chipped and ground. Other members of the Department also allowed themselves to be enlisted in the case of some specimens of particular obscurity.

Dr. William Sturtevant and Dr. Samuel Stanley at the National Museum of Natural History, Smithsonian Institution, provided valuable advice, as did Dr. Bethune Gibson, Head of that Museum's Conservation Laboratory. It was she who advised us on all the intricate problems of cleaning and repair.

Exhibition of this choice selection of Indian objects would have been impossible without the cleaning and restoration activities undertaken by the Cincinnati Art Museum's Conservation Department and the volunteers and students who assisted. Mrs. Elisabeth Batchelor, Assistant Conservator, supervised the project, developing new techniques and employing old ones to facilitate cleaning and repair of dozens of objects. Volunteers and students involved with this project were: Nancy Teepen, Joan Gilder, Sophia Prevey, Marianne Schwab, Pat Cohl, Mary Carol Moses, Alice Webster, Mark A. Mignery, Carol Winter, Clinton Allen, Greg Rusk, and Debbie Traves.

Two volunteers, Joan Gilder and Nadine Bradfut, converted information on cards into an indispensable typescript of nearly 50,000 objects that assisted sorting and classifying.

Noel Martin, Museum Designer, assisted by Dana and Reid Martin, produced not only the handsome scheme for the exhibition's installation, but also designed the catalogue and all typographic material accompanying this Bicentennial project. Publicity and promotion were developed by Assistant Director Betty L. Zimmerman and Jane A. Durrell, Assistant for Press Relations. Typescript of the catalogue was undertaken by Constance C. Leavitt.

A teaching exhibition incorporating a Discovery Room, slide presentation area and craftsmanship demonstrations, to accompany the exhibition at the Museum, was organized by Curator of Education Roslynne V. Wilson, with Museum docents and Education Department staff participating in this unique educational venture.

The abiding interest of Curators Shine and Meyer in our American Indian collection, coupled with hours of research, sorting, and cataloguing, were essential to realize this exhibition and catalogue. The Cincinnati Art Museum acknowledges with gratitude the dedication, persistence, expertise, and affection of many individuals for these works of art and for the great culture that produced them.

Millard F. Rogers, Jr.
Director

217

10

THE NORTHWEST COAST

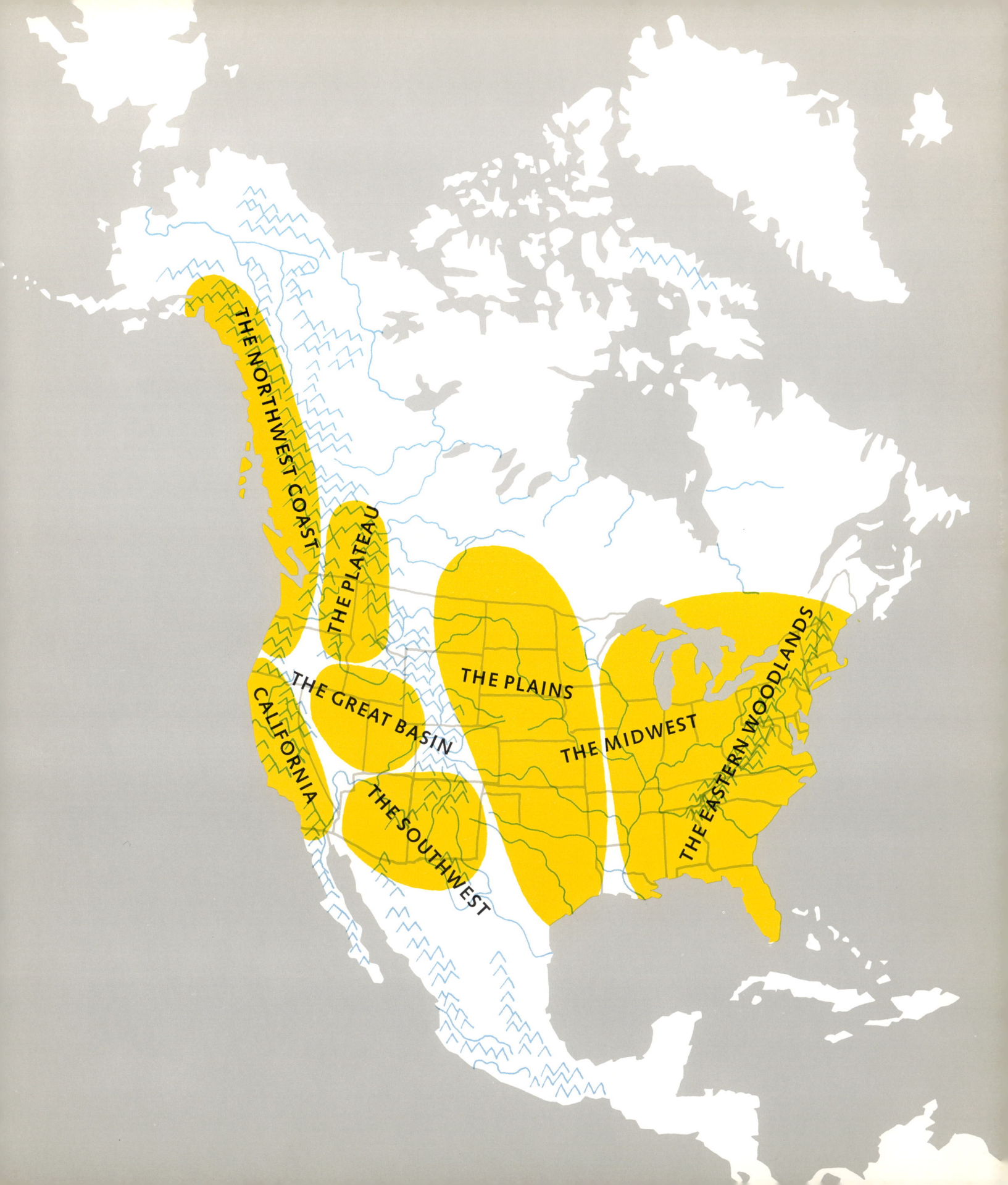

THE PLATEAU

THE PLAINS

THE GREAT BASIN

CALIFORNIA

THE MIDWEST

THE SOUTHWEST

THE EASTERN WOODLANDS

Art of the First Americans: in Search of the Past

For the Centennial Exposition in Philadelphia in 1876, a dedicated group of Cincinnati ladies organized a Women's Centennial Committee to exhibit works of art created by women artists of Cincinnati. They raised money, assembled paintings, woodcarving, needlework and ceramics, hired a carpenter to pack and to install, hired a custodian to guard the exhibit, brought everything back at the close of the Exposition, and had $384.22 left over. Flown with success, they met on January 18, 1877, to disband the Centennial Committee and regroup as the Women's Art Museum Association for the purpose of founding in Cincinnati, not only an Art Museum, but an Art School as well.

By the time the Cincinnati Art Museum opened its doors in 1886, its collection had already been accumulating since 1881. The very first acquisition recorded in a large red Donation Book was a pottery vessel, recovered from a recently discovered Indian village site, of then undatable antiquity, between Madisonville (now part of Cincinnati) and the edge of the bluff overlooking the Little Miami River.

In fact, the first three acquisitions recorded in the Donation Book were Madisonville pots given to the Women's Art Museum Association in 1881 for the still-to-be-built Museum by the Honorable Judge Joseph Cox. Judge Cox (1822-1900), brought by his family to Cincinnati in 1831, studied medicine with his father, Dr. Hiram Cox, switched to the law and had a successful career as a lawyer and a judge, with a wide range of interests, one of which was the archaeology of the Ohio-Mississippi valley. He was one of the associates of Dr. Charles L. Metz who led his fellow members of the Madisonville Literary and Scientific Society to recover from oblivion the evidence of the ancient occupation of the Little Miami valley.

The founding of the Museum coincided with the turn of interest in the pre-European inhabitants of the Americas from antiquarian curiosity to scientific enquiry. A good deal of surface collecting plus treasure hunting where mounds had been broken open by the plough had been going on since the early nineteenth century and even earlier in the East. In 1879 and 1880, however, the members of the Madisonville Literary and Scientific Society paid out of their own pockets to hire workmen for the pick and shovel work of a careful excavation of the Madisonville site, and rewarded themselves by sharing out the artifacts uncovered. The records of the many artifacts from that excavation now in the Cincinnati Art Museum indicate that the members of the Society traded among themselves and also deposited some of the artifacts in the Cabinet of the Society. No inventory of the Cabinet has been located, but when Harry Zerring bequeathed his Indian collection to the Museum in 1918, he left a record that some of the artifacts had once been in the Cabinet of the Literary and Scientific Society while others had come into his hands from the collections of C. F. Low, Judge Cox, R. O. Collis and other members. Casual though this may seem today, Dr. Charles Louis Metz (1847-1926) of Madisonville was sufficiently aware of the more advanced archaeological ideas of his day to conduct a fairly well-ordered excavation with attention to levels, to measurements and to non-artifactural features like storage pits, burning sites, etc.

Many of the members of the Madisonville Literary and Scientific Society were also members of the Cincinnati Society of Natural History, and the Natural History Society helped with the excavation and in 1880 published in its *Journal* a three-part article by Charles F. Low on the day-to-day excavation of the Madisonville site, illustrated with precise drawings of some of the more striking finds. Low also deposited in the Museum Library a notebook containing drawings for some of these illustrations plus a great many more drawings of artifacts found at Madisonville and in areas nearby, some presumably by his hand and some which appear to be by other hands, plus photographs of some of the Madisonville material and of objects from farther afield such as a stone mask "Found by J. McConnel, Ross County, Ohio," and another mask, ownership unspecified but bearing on the reverse the name and address of a photographer in Chillicothe, Ohio.

In 1882 the Peabody Museum of Harvard University, under the direction of Professor Putnam, became active in this excavation, receiving a share of the artifacts, but retaining Dr. Metz as Director of the excavation.

Thanks to the efforts of the Women's Art Museum Association, much of the Madisonville material was attracted to the Museum-to-be. In 1888 Dr. Metz himself brought in the Madisonville material collected by his friend and colleague, R. O. Collis, as an indefinite loan. This was purchased for the Museum in 1908 by Harry Levy, and other pieces came in one or two at a time from individuals who had participated in the excavation or whose friends had. But the Women's Art Museum Association members, with true museum zeal, did not confine their efforts to local material. In 1885 they bought selected pieces from the infant Rookwood Pottery in Cincinnati and traded them to the United States National Museum for Pueblo pottery collected in the Southwest by James Stevenson, Major Powell, the Mindeleff brothers and others under the auspices of the Bureau of Ethnology of the Smithsonian Institution.

That collectors of that era did a good deal of swapping and perhaps also buying is borne out by the collection of Thomas Cleneay of whom virtually nothing is known except that he is listed in Cincinnati Directories from 1851 to 1887. The collection he first lent, then bequeathed to the Museum upon his death in 1887, amounted to no less than 20,000 items and probably a good many more than that, because a benefaction of such staggering proportions was beyond the capacity of the then Museum staff to cope with, and no detailed inventory was compiled until fifty years later. A substantial amount of material, shifting between exhibition cases and storage trays was, by that time, no longer certainly identifiable with the Cleneay collection. The scant surviving documentation concerning the Cleneay collection indicates that he got his artifacts not only from personal foraging in spots like Columbia (the first white settlement in Hamilton County, at the mouth of the Little Miami, approximately where Cincinnati's Lunken Airport is now), Pendleton (approximately at the foot of Delta Avenue, Cincinnati), Storrs Township (another section of the present Cincinnati riverfront), "opposite Aurora, Indiana," and so on, but also from "A man at Columbia, O.," "The Wild Kentuckian," "Mr. Terrell, Valley Junction," and others. Cleneay painstakingly wrote with India ink on every piece from Terrell's collection, "Mr. Terrell, Valley Junction, Indiana." Valley Junction, however, is not only extinct by now, but probably was not in Indiana even then, but in Ohio. The only nearby Valley Junction that has come to light was a stop on the Whitewater Valley R.R., 17 miles west of Cincinnati. Who Mr. Terrell was is now buried in the mists of the past, as is the identity of "The Wild Kentuckian." Any devotee of local history who can provide this information will be cordially received.

Cleneay was collecting from Mr. Terrell and others in the early 1870's, but some of his material had been collected far earlier than that. Some of his pieces came to the Museum carefully marked in faded ink, "Dorfuelle's Museum/Ohmer's Museum 1874." Ohmer is still obscure: Cincinnati Directories between 1862 and 1872 list a John P. Ohmer as proprietor of, first a confectionery, then a saloon, then a zoological garden at several addresses on east Front Street. But "Dorfuelle's" Museum can refer only to the Western Museum, one of the first scientific museums in the United States, started by the pioneer doctor Daniel Drake and his friends in 1818 with collecting relics of the ancient inhabitants of the country one of the expressed intentions. Dr. Drake contributed Indian artifacts from his own collection, some of which may have come from his teacher, Dr. Goforth, and the founding members collected more. The first curator of the collection was Dr. Robert Best, another pioneer physician, and in 1823 Joseph Dorfeuille (born in France about 1790) was added to the staff. In 1823 the founders, finding the museum a financial burden, attempted to sell it. Failing that, they gave it to Dorfeuille to run as a commercial enterprise with the proviso that the original subscribers would be admitted free. Thereafter it became known as Dorfeuille's Museum and continued to be so called even after Dorfeuille moved to Brooklyn, N. Y., about 1838 and it was annexed to the rival Franks Museum. In the 1850's it became more of an art gallery than a general museum and there is no record of what became of the Indian collection, but it is thought that they must have been sold piecemeal to private collectors, which would account for the items in Cleneay's collection. It is conceivable that some of these might have come originally from Dr. Drake's own collection, but there is nothing now to show whether this is so.

In 1888, C. W. Riggs, a dealer with a Chicago and later a New York address, deposited in the Museum on loan a vast quantity of pottery which he said he had collected in Crittenden, St. Francis and Poinsette Counties of Arkansas. Only the number of boxes was recorded, and this fluctuated from month to month as he shipped in still more boxes and called for the return of earlier shipments. One of the few individual items recorded was one of the recalls: a stunning bowl in the form of a man's head which he ordered dispatched to W. H. Holmes at the Field Collection in Chicago. This must have been the eminent archaeologist who became Director of the Bureau of American Ethnology in 1902. Six hundred and sixty-five pieces of Riggs' pottery were bought by Dr. S. C. Heighway of Cincinnati who was made Honorary Curator of the Archaeological Collection in 1889. They remained in the Museum as a loan until they were made a gift in 1937.

Riggs himself traded additional Arkansas pottery to the Museum for material from the vast Cleneay collection, and it is painful to speculate what Riggs, who seems to have had a very shrewd eye, acquired at that time when almost nothing was understood of the significance of the archaeological material.

1888 also marks the beginning of an influx of material from the Northwest Coast. There was a gift from Dr. and Mrs. William Wallace Seely of Cincinnati which included a good deal of the paraphernalia of a Chilkat shaman, acquired from Winthrop W. Fisk in Juneau, Alaska; and in 1889 the United States National Museum gave the Cincinnati Art Museum material collected by James G. Swan and others in Alaska at the same time that it gave a large number of baskets collected in Alaska, the Southwest, the Plains, Plateau and Great Basin. The Seelys gave more material from the Northwest Coast in 1889; William Howard Doane, a collector of musical instruments, lent Northwest Coast drums, rattles and whistles, later to become a gift; and in 1893 Lucien Wulsin a prominent businessman with wide interests in the civic and cultural amenities of Cincinnati, lent some 44 objects from the Northwest Coast, which were made a gift many years later. His sister-in-law, Anna Roelker, apparently also went through a Northwest Coast

861, 863, 864, 865

phase: some of her pieces came to the Museum in 1918 via the collection of Harry Zerring.

Interest in the arts and crafts of the first Americans had by that time expanded far beyond the intellectual puzzle of buried remote antiquity to appreciation of the traditional forms still being produced by living Indians: the striking pottery of the Southwest; the exquisitely functional basketry that served for everything from protection against the weather to collecting food and even to cooking it; the finely worked skins, brilliantly decorated with paint, dyed porcupine quills, feathers and beads with which the Indians clothed themselves and carried their belongings. General Manning Ferguson Force, a Civil War veteran and a prominent Cincinnati lawyer and judge, had amassed a large collection of such recent material, including the superb painted buffalo hide on the cover of this catalogue, which he lent to the Museum in 1888 and made a gift in 1894. His collection also included a number of local archaeological artifacts, some of them from the Madisonville site, and these continued steadily to trickle into the Museum: Judge Cox gave additional Madisonville pieces in 1889; the members of the Cincinnati Museum Association dug at several spots in Hamilton County and collected farther afield in the Ohio Valley; G. A. Katzenberger contributed material from Darke County in 1890.

1890 was also the year that Robert Clarke, a Cincinnati publisher, brought to the Museum as loans two extraordinary engraved stone tablets: the Cincinnati Tablet now belonging to the Cincinnati Historical Society, and the Waverly (or Clarke-Hurst) Tablet which belonged to him and was given to the Museum in 1939 by his niece, Mrs. Eugene Galt. The Cincinnati Tablet which was found in one of the complex of mounds along the river terrace that is now Third Street, was the subject of a storm of the wildest speculations during the nineteenth century, but these tablets, of which only about a dozen are known, have taken their place as a still enigmatic product of the phase of Indian culture called Adena after the estate of Governor Thomas Worthington at Chillicothe where the type site for this phase was found. Governor Worthington's grandson, William Neal King of Cincinnati, was another contributor to the Museum's Indian collection, giving in 1906 and 1922 Pueblo pottery and baskets from many areas. The great interest in baskets was probably started by Matilda Stevenson, wife of James Stevenson. Some of the baskets she collected came to the Museum via the United States National Museum in 1885 and 1889. The Museum's baskets are all less than a hundred years old, vegetal fibers having a poor survival rate except in a few exceptionally dry localities, but basket making is an older art than pottery, and the winnowing baskets of the Great Basin, for instance, that were collected while still in use in the 1870's probably perpetuated forms of many thousand years earlier.

In 1907 James W. Bullock added to the basket collection. In 1911 more baskets were given by Mrs. S. Herbert Randall and by Eleanor I. Earnshaw, while Philip Hinkle, a banker and Honorary Curator of the Archaeological Collection from 1905 to 1934, added to the archaeological collection, and Mrs. Charles Fleischmann gave Indian dolls and figurines. Baskets were given in 1913 by William Watts Taylor, Manager of Rookwood Pottery. From Harry Zerring in 1918 came a great deal more archaeological material formerly in the collections of Dr. Metz, Charles F. Low, Judge Cox and other stalwarts of the Madisonville Literary and Scientific Society. In 1929 the Museum bought from Mrs. B. P. Wagner of Sidney, Ohio, her collection of pottery and ornaments from Casas Grandes, a Pueblo-like site just across the border in Mexico. And in 1937, Dr. Heighway made a gift not only of the Arkansas pottery he had bought from Riggs, but several thousand other archaeological pieces including some more choice Madisonville objects.

Also in 1937, Amelia Elizabeth White of Santa Fe, New Mexico, unexpectedly bestowed on the Museum Southwest pottery, jewelry and textiles. Until the White gift, almost all of the Indian material with the exception of the Arkansas and Casas Grandes pottery, had come from Cincinnatians to their own museum. Miss White, however, a Bryn Mawr graduate, a daughter of Horace White, proprietor and editor of the *Chicago Tribune,* was a New Yorker. She had gone to Santa Fe in 1934 on her way to witness an eclipse in California. With her sister, she bought property in Santa Fe and became interested in the Indians and in their crafts. She became involved in the Bureau of Indian Affairs and she also started a shop, the Gallery of American Indian Art, in New York to sell Indian crafts, the first of its kind. In 1937, toward the end of the Depression, the shop was not doing well, so she closed it and distributed the inventory among a number of museums, including the Cincinnati Art Museum. She died in 1972, aged 94, and it is in her house in Santa Fe that the present School of American Research is located.

The donations continued, and it has not been possible to name them all. In 1942 Mrs. Philip C. Swing gave a painting on muslin from the northern Plains, adding to the two given by General Force in 1894 and another purchased from the painter Joseph H. Sharp. In 1943, Pueblo pottery from Dr. Daniel Cook; 1945, Pueblo pottery from Mary Hanna, who is better known for her gift of superb European paintings and a wing to house them; 1948, Alaskan material from the Dunham family and Hopi needlework from Mrs. Russell Wilson; 1954, the Kiowa drawings from Merritt Boyle. The list of benefactors who, from the founding of the Museum, have contributed toward its Indian collection is indeed impressive, and it is to their fascination with the art of the first Americans and to the thousands of years of patient Indian skill, that we owe this present exhibition.

Carolyn R. Shine,
Registrar and Assistant General Curator

Mary L. Meyer,
Curator of Costumes and Textiles

Conservation

An ethnographical exhibition of this type and scale is an exciting challenge to the modern conservator, requiring as it does the use of techniques new to the conservation profession. Indeed a few of the methods used in the preparation of these Indian artifacts were of necessity experimental in nature as I shall describe later.

From the vast and rich collection of American Indian artifacts in storage at the Cincinnati Art Museum, it was necessary to prepare more than a hundred baskets, a hundred leather and textile objects and numerous objects of stone, bone, metal, shell, skin, wood, feathers and clay. This major conservation programme was begun in April 1975 and continued until the end of the year when the final selection for the exhibition was made.

By far the most time consuming task was the cleaning of the baskets. Not only had they been stored for decades, becoming brittle and collecting dirt and grime, but also at some point in their history nearly every one had been coated with a thick layer of shellac. This held in the dirt and obscured the original colour and decoration. There were three major problems: the removal of the shellac, the removal of the dirt, and the softening of the dry hard fibres. Of course no two Indian baskets are identical. To restore each individual basket to its original condition required subtle variations in the technical procedures employed. The weave, the type of material used and the chemical composition of the natural dyes used for decoration had to be taken into consideration.

Most leather objects cannot be cleaned with any type of solvent because this leaves them stiff and unnatural. Unfortunately the light coloured suede side of the leather is especially susceptible to dirt and at the same time soft and delicate. Until very recently this combination of characteristics had made leather cleaning very perilous. About five years ago conservators turned to the industrial techniques of the airbrasive machine. With modifications to suit our special purpose, this machine has proved to be not only very effective but also very efficient. Basically the machine functions like an ordinary drawing eraser except that the erasing is done by a small but powerful jet of powdered sodium bicarbonate or tiny glass beads which are forced by compressed air through a nozzle held in the operator's hand. The powder gently abrades the surface and removes any dirt without injuring the surface.

The first machine used was kindly lent to the Art Museum by the Geology Department of the University of Cincinnati. Later a generous donation enabled the Museum to purchase a new airbrasive machine and air compressor. A good deal of experimentation was necessary with different air pressures, amount and kinds of powder, and different nozzles, so that each object could be treated individually as is necessary for such delicate material.

The whole vast field of ethnographical conservation is a new area of specialization for the Cincinnati Art Museum. Indeed throughout the world the urgent need to develop this branch of conservation has only recently begun to be realized. For the conservator it is a demanding and interesting field. At every stage he has to rely on his knowledge of a wide variety of materials and techniques. The international authority and Head Conservator of the Anthropology Conservation Lab of the Smithsonian Institution in Washington, Mrs. Bethune Gibson in a letter of August 26, 1975, stated the situation clearly: "... very little has yet been published on ethnographic conservation and the conservator must depend on his own tests and experiments."

Almost every day presented a new problem. There were the very brittle fishskins that had to be softened and reshaped again; feathers covered with dirt had to be cleaned without breaking the barbs; shells were covered with shellac and had to be consolidated; beads and pottery were encrusted with dirt; textiles were threadbare and stained; wood, horn, skin and clay objects had to be pieced together.

Almost all the artifacts were in urgent need of treatment if they were to be preserved for the future. Within a few years some of the objects may have become very difficult or impossible to repair, if conservation had not taken place at this time.

This exciting Bicentennial exhibition not only serves the immediate goal of public display, but it also focuses our attention on the crucial need to preserve through continual careful conservation procedures these precious artifacts representing the art of the very first Americans. Without such care many of these objects would simply not survive to help us celebrate our Tricentennial in another hundred years time.

Elisabeth Batchelor,
Assistant Conservator

The Recent Past

Until recently, American Indian art works were exhibited in museums of natural history, beside dinosaur bones, insect displays and stuffed animals. Art museums, on the other hand, tended to concentrate on the paintings, sculpture, pottery, textiles, etc., produced by the "higher civilizations" of Europe and Asia and the Mediterranean area. Implicit in this division was the definition of products of high civilization as art, and the implicit conception that the works of other cultures constituted something other than art. In recent years, art museums, in increasing numbers, have been displaying the works of other cultures. The present exhibition will impress the viewer with the fact that art, and artists, are a part of the life of mankind, wherever and under whatever circumstances he lives. The native Americans illustrate this fact very well.

The life styles and circumstances of the native North American were much more variable than most people realize. In what is now the continental United States, the Indian developed ways of making his livelihood in such diverse environments as deserts, mountains, river bottoms, grassy plains and hardwood forests. To each environment, man brought different knowledge, tools and techniques. And each of these environments offered different materials for man to work with. Using his know-how and his inventiveness, the Indian fashioned from the animals, plants and minerals available to him artifacts that not only served to maintain life but also pleased him aesthetically. What he fashioned continues to please us.

Because artifacts are produced by people living under different conditions, an understanding of the cultures from which the items derive adds to our appreciation of what we see. For example, virtually all known cultures have produced baskets. But baskets are made of local materials, designed to serve particular functions, and are decorated according to local traditions. In the present exhibit there are baskets of grasses, reeds, cactus fibers, twigs and various types of wood splints. Decorations are achieved by varying the weaving technique or the color of the woven elements, or by attaching materials such as shells or feathers. The various shapes of the baskets are determined primarily by their uses: a Hopi food tray (474*), an Apache water bottle (467), a Paiute carrying basket (267) and a Pomo baby carrier (141) . . . all are designed to meet specific needs of the people, using the materials and techniques available to them.

Another factor influencing the local manufacture is also apparent, namely, the influence that one culture has on another. The Indians had borrowed ideas and tools and techniques from each other long before the European landed on the American continents. Indian versatility and adaptiveness become very ap-

32

*Numbers in parentheses refer to Catalogue Numbers.

parent when we see the inventiveness with which he adopted and applied materials of European manufacture and made them into things specifically Indian. Navajo wool blankets and silver work, Woodlands and Plains beadwork, the development of new pottery styles by Pueblo Indians, and adaptation of the back-carried cradle board to the Spanish introduced horse (245): all are combinations of Indian and European elements.

This exhibition is arranged according to the culture groupings of the different geographical regions of North America. In each area the environment has influenced the life style of the inhabitants and so the form as well as the materials of their art.

The Northwest Coast

Indians of the Northwest Coast inhabit an area of tall hardwood forests, abrupt mountains, rushing rivers and large coastal islands. In the past they lived a very bountiful life—unusually so for people without the techniques of food production. Their ingenuity in harvesting the vast amount of salmon and olachen fish that annually swam up the rivers in droves to spawn, plus their ability to process the same for storage, provided them with a staple food supply. To this food they added large sea mammals (such as seals, walrus, and in some cases even whales), land mammals, a variety of plant foods including roots and berries, and large ocean fish such as halibut the size of which is reflected in the size of the hooks used in their capture (60-65). With such relatively stable and abundant food, the Indians were able to live in sedentary villages, composed of large wooden houses, each of which held several families. In addition, they were able to produce for their own use and pleasure items of woven, carved and molded manufacture of a unique and (to our way of thinking) rather flamboyant art style in which animal forms predominate. To view some of it whets the appetite for more.

Although horn spoons are widespread in North America (particularly west of the Mississippi), the Northwest spoons are executed with more attention and concern to their decorative aspects. (Compare, for example, the horn spoons in the Southwest and Plains areas of the exhibit.) The technique of working horn, as done by North American Indians, involved softening the horn in hot water and molding it, much as one might do with a plastic. To the process, the Northwest Coast Indian added carving and inlaying (52). The occurrence of very large spoons throughout native North America (generally made of wood in the Eastern Woodlands) comes as something of a surprise to most contemporary Americans. A consideration of cooking techniques helps us to understand the convenience of this utensil. The common method of cooking was to boil a variety of foods in a large container. To this large soup pot, each individual carried his own spoon, dipped in, and went and sat down with both his liquid and his solid food in one container from which he drank the broth and extracted the solids with his fingers.

Northwest Coast Indians are particularly noted for their carving. Every American school child has heard of "totem poles", which, like feathered headdresses and tipis, have become symbols of Indians in general. Totem poles are, however, specific to the Northwest Coast. Such a totem pole represents the geneology of an individual in terms of the families he or she is descended from. The families are named after different animals and the totem poles represent the families by the animals. Very large totem poles were carved out of wood, similar to the more delicate ones of slate represented in this exhibit (68-70).

Other striking forms of Northwest Coast sculpture include both the masks and the boxes. The boxes are constructed in an unusual manner. The initial technique is like that applied to horn, namely, soaking the wood to make it more malleable. A plank or board of wood is subjected to warm water, grooves bevelled for the corners, and the whole then wrapped around so that the ends of the plank join. Holes are prepared along the seam for lashing, and the ends are then sewn together (41, 67). The boxes, usually of cedar wood, are sometimes further ornamented by carving and/or, as in the case of masks, the inlaying of shell, stone or opercula (41, 43).

Masks were carved to represent mythical beings and worn in enacting folktales and religious dramas. The faces are strong and bold, as befits gods and ancestors, and their impressiveness enhanced by the inlays and the colors painted on. Additional vitality was achieved by the construction of masks with moveable parts (27). The enactment of a sacred tale by fire-light using such masks must have been awesome indeed.

The work in wood and horn is so spectacular that the basketry of the Northwest Coast has tended to be overlooked. However, the skill exhibited in this medium should not be disregarded. Using grasses, bark and splintered wood, the Indians created baskets that were appropriate for many uses: for gathering clams (106, 108) or berries (94, 103, 104); for storage (97, 105); even as cups (91, 92) and for cooking. Unlike the carvings, the basketry featured primarily geometric designs rather than animal forms.

There are three types of items here that merit special attention before leaving the Northwest Coast: the Chilkat blanket (13), the silver bracelets (16-25), and the paraphernalia of Skundoo the shaman (11, 12, 14, 28-33).

So far as we know, Chilkat blankets were produced before

contact with non-Native American cultures. These fabrics were very highly valued by the Indians of the Northwest Coast, where ordinary clothing was not made of wool but of bark. The Chilkat blanket was made on an upright frame from which cedar bark, intertwined with the wool of mountain goat, was suspended as the warp of the fabric. Across this warp was woven spun goat's wool in its natural color or dyed black, blue or yellow. The designs are the stylized animal forms that are characteristic of the area. Such blankets were, in general, worn by people of high rank on ceremonial occasions.

Silver work was never a characteristic enterprise of Northwest Coast Indians. But the little that they did produce is quite different from the Southwestern silver work and just as distinctively Northwest in terms of design as the Navajo silver work is Navajo. The designs on the Northwest Coast bracelets are, as in their other art work, primarily animal forms and geometric shapes. The animals look rather like "flattened out" totem pole animals. The Navajo work, on the other hand, though it does contain thunderbirds, is decorated mainly with zigzag lines, arrows, stylized suns, roped borders, and so forth. Examples of Northwest Coast silver work are rare and we are fortunate to have some here for comparison and contrast with the more generally known southwestern silver material.

Skundoo was a shaman (religious man), reputedly of great power. He practiced his art of calling on the supernatural beings for aid, using items that would please or entice them. Skundoo's mantles of moosehide (11) and of tradecloth and cotton (12), unlike ordinary garments, were decorated with paintings of birds, animals and man. When worn in combination with one or another of his headdress masks (28-33), the effect must have been dramatic enough to attract the attention of both the spirits and the human beings present. The addition of his necklace of bone and ivory pendants (14) which would have rattled as he moved must have made him impressive indeed.

California

California offered man a warm climate together with the sea, rivers, deserts and mountains. Indians of the California culture area were not tillers of the soil, but they were nevertheless village Indians. Like the people of the Northwest Coast, the California Indians had developed skills that enabled them to harvest, process and store a natural product in quantities sufficient to provide them with a food staple throughout the year. Whereas for the Northwest Coast the harvest was fish, in California it was the acorn. Because of the high tannic acid content of most varieties of acorn, they are not edible by man in sufficient quantities to form a staple food unless they are processed.

The processing in California generally involved removing the hulls of the nuts, pulverizing them in a mortar and pestle, and then pouring hot water through the pulp to carry off the acid. The end product could be made into a mush for immediate consumption, or dried and stored to be eaten later in the form of a mush or a baked bread. Supplemented by fish, game animals and other wild plant foods, the native Californian was provided with a food supply that enabled him to build permanent villages and live a sedentary life.

The importance of basketry to the Californian is indicated here by the variety of forms, skill in weaving and the attention paid to decoration. Baskets were used throughout the area in most of the activities involved in the processing of acorns. Gathering involved the use of large carrying baskets (110). In pounding, baskets were used to prevent spillage from the mortar (122). In leaching, water was boiled in watertight baskets by dropping hot stones in the water (124). The cooking of mush was also done in baskets with hot stones. In many parts of California, the leaching process itself was done by placing the pulp in a porous basket and pouring the hot water through. And finally, the dried flour was stored in baskets.

Basketry had other utilitarian uses in California, as, for example, for catching and processing fish (see the fish scoop, 139, and the basket for drying fish, 138), for head gear (109, 112, 120) and for carrying infants (113, 141).

The utility of the basket to California Indians is evident. But it should be equally evident that it was created as an item of aesthetic pleasure as well. The addition of feathers and shells and beads attest to the fact (126-136). Indeed, California basketry is regarded by many experts as the epitome of North American Indian basketry art.

The Plains

Plains Indian culture as we know it historically is a way of life that developed in the historical period as a consequence of European influences in North America. The Plains area was a vast grass land with long, meandering rivers and infrequent stands of trees. Although the area abounded in game (including notably deer, antelope, bear and buffalo), the Indian could not hunt game effectively enough on foot to enable him to develop large populations based on hunting as the mainstay of life. Consequently, in the prehistoric period the Plains was inhabited by peoples with two very different types of life styles. Along the river beds lived corn-raising village Indians. And in the grassy ranges between the rivers and in the areas too far north for corn, small bands of Indians roamed, gathering wild plant foods, hunting available animals, and living in temporary dwellings constructed on pole frameworks—a form of housing that could easily be rebuilt upon moving and which formed the prototype for the historic tipi. The advent of the horse, combined with the pressures exerted on Indian populations by the expansion of the colonial settlements, brought revolutionary changes.

The horse was introduced to the area by the Spanish, from whom the Indians also adopted the horse trappings. The advantages to nomadic hunting peoples of an animal so well suited for both riding and carrying burdens resulted in its being readily adopted in the southern Plains, and its rather rapid spread throughout the whole Plains area. With the horse, man could take efficient advantage of the abundant game the area had to offer. This he did, with particular emphasis on the literally millions of buffalo, utilizing his flesh for food, his hide for the tipi and for warm and sometimes elegant robes (158-160), furs for bedding, the hooves for glue, the skin in the form of rawhide to make containers (*parfleche,* see e.g. 244), and horn and bone for various implements.

So successful was this life style that the Plains became a refuge area for various tribes being pressured out of their previous territories by settlers, as well as by other Indian groups. The Iroquois pushing west in search of new sources of furs pushed the Chippewa (or Ojibway), who in turn pushed the Sioux out of what is now Minnesota, and the Sioux shoved the Cheyenne ahead of them. Other tribes were lured into the area by this new life style that was a richer one than they had had before. Shoshones moved out of the west to become Comanches, forcing the Apaches into the Southwest. And the Comanches were ultimately driven south of the Arkansas river by the Kiowa, who were being pressured from the north by the Dakota and Cheyenne.

Each of the various tribes contributed to the development of Plains culture, and each of them had their own variant of it. From 1800 to 1890, the time period predominantly represented here, Plains culture was at its height. As an effect of their mobility and their competing for buffalo and for territory—first with each other and later with the white man—warfare became a major pursuit and to be a warrior a proud and glorious thing. The importance of war is illustrated by the magnificent headdress (171) that became a mark of distinction in the Plains, and by the elaborate attention paid to the manufacture of quivers and gun cases (228-235). We see the significance of warfare to the Indian in his paintings (159-170) in which he depicts historical events in his life.

While the men distinguished themselves as hunters and warriors, the women also enriched their sphere of life. Previous to the introduction of glass beads, a principal means of decorating the buckskin clothing and moccasins had consisted of applying porcupine quills in designs on the soft leather. Although this technique remained on into the nineteenth century (184 ff.) glass beads, which were easier to handle, readily acquired in quantities through trade, and available in a variety of pleasing colors rapidly began to replace the quill. Plains Indian women became inventive and skilled in beading, and we can appreciate the artistry, patience and long hours that went into the manufacture of the clothing and containers exhibited here. (Note especially 160, 175, 183, 191). Note also that the floral designs, so popular in the Eastern Woodlands, were carried over into the Plains.

Finally, the importance of religion to the Plains Indians is, once again, reflected in their art. The major annual religious celebration of Plains Indians was the Sun Dance, depictions of which, for example, are prominent in the paintings (161).

The Eastern Woodlands

Indians east of the Mississippi river were, by and large, village Indians who lived by raising corn, beans and squash, gathering nuts and berries and other wild plant foods, fishing the rivers and streams, and hunting the animals of the hardwood forests that covered much of the area. Although much of the items of native manufacture disappeared early in the historic period, we can get some sense of the variation and skill in their technology from examining the archaeological materials on display.

Some items of native manufacture did, however, remain on into the nineteenth century. Prior to European settlement, Indians of the Northeast used birchbark in a number of ways. Most of us have some familiarity with the birchbark canoe (the prototype of our contemporary canoe), but the use of bark, decorated with quill work, for containers is not so well known (316, 317). For the Northeast, bark containers served many of the same functions that pottery and basketry served elsewhere.

Eastern Woodlands Indians also made baskets, however, and basketry techniques continued on into the nineteenth and twentieth centuries, particularly in the southeast, where they were produced for trade (286-288). Cane splints were a favored material, with designs of geometric shape. The elbow basket (284) is a form unique to the area.

As in the Plains, bead work became a decorative technique that partially eclipsed the use of quills and that, along with ribbon applique, was highly developed in the hands of the women (294, 297, 302-306, 309-312). Before the introduction of wool yarns, women of the eastern tribes wove sashes out of plant fibers, sometimes mixed with the hair of wild animals. Wool was adapted for these garments in the historic period (299-301).

The small elbow pipes are of interest especially because it was this type of pipe (rather than, for example, a tubular pipe) that became the prototype of the common forms in use in Europe and America today. The snowshoe (315) is another device that is of interest because it was an invention of the American Indian.

The Great Basin

The Great Basin area of North America is a high, dry area for the most part, with plants and animals edible to man being rather sparse. With a hunting and gathering technology, man roamed the area on foot in bands of twenty-five to thirty people, subsisting mainly on wild plants and small animals. Such a life style does not permit the accumulation of many possessions. Housing consisted of temporary pole and brush shelters; clothing of a small fur or fiber apron for women, a breechcloth for men, and fiber sandals for both. The elaborate pottery of the Southwest, wooden products of the Northwest Coast, and the decorative leather clothing of the Plains and Woodlands were impractical and even generally impossible.

But in the art of basketry, which was light to carry and readily made with the materials at hand, the Basin Indians came into their own. Baskets were used for carrying (267), cooking (268), and even clothing (264). As in the case of California, the relationship of basketry to food is striking. The basic food supply in most of the Basin area was various seeds. Women gathered these, using fans (266) to beat the seeds into large conical baskets (265). The collecting basket then served as a carrying basket which the women carried on their backs by means of a line wrapped around their shoulders or their foreheads. In the case of the latter, the conical hat (264) protected the flesh from chafing. Further, seeds were roasted in basket trays (such as 268) by filling the tray with seeds, adding stones heated on a fire, and shaking the two together.

The Southwest

The great desert region of the North American southwest had two different types of life style in the immediate prehistoric period: the settled farmer living in towns (Pueblos) and the roaming hunter and gatherer, some of whose descendents are the contemporary Navajos.

The Pueblo Indians (Hopi, Zuni, Santa Clara, San Ildefonso, etc.) selected locations for their towns primarily on the basis of available water supplies, and perhaps also with an eye to defense. The towns were located in canyons or river valleys or on the tops of the spectacular rock mesas of the area. Corn, beans and squash were raised for sustenance, to which were added various wild plant and animal foods. In addition, the Pueblo Indians raised cotton, from which the men wove tex-

327

tiles for clothing. Although they adopted imported textiles rather early, the custom of weaving belts remains to the present day (433-435).

The Pueblo Indians are particularly noted for their fine pottery which was manufactured by a coiling process and without benefit of a potters wheel. Prehistoric village Indians of the Southwest were making pottery as early as A.D. 500. The earliest wares were crude and unpainted; but well before the historic period, the southwestern Indians had developed pottery-making into a rich art form. The prehistoric wares had already assumed a variety of shapes, serving a variety of purposes; storage jars (326) pitchers, water jars and bowls with many uses (318, 322, 325). For designs (with the exception of the Mimbres area), geometric motifs were generally preferred over life forms. Painting was done primarily in either red or black—colors that continue to dominate in modern Pueblo pottery. The importance of pottery to the Pueblo area is indicated not only by its abundance and variety, but also by the fact that it was customary to "kill" a pot and place it with the dead in order that the deceased would have use of it in the afterlife. "Killing" was done by tapping a hole in the bottom of the vessel (325, 346).

In historic times, although each Pueblo had its own traditional designs, it is possible to recognize some characteristics shared throughout the region. The ware is generally rather thick-bodied, slipped but unglazed, with bowls and jars the predominant shapes. The painted designs consist of geometrical shapes and graceful stylized life forms. The colors present a soft appearance, with white, cream, buff, black and orange the main hues. Some particularly fine examples of Pueblo pottery in this collection are 352, 357, 376, 394.

The black wares made by Pueblo Indians are produced by using the same clays but firing the pots in a "reducing" or high carbon atmosphere. Santa Clara black ware (369-374) was produced by the early nineteenth century. About a century later (1919) the process was reinvented at San Ildefonso by Maria Martinez and her husband Julian. Maria formed the pots and her husband decorated them and fired them. A measure of the genius of Julian is his having developed a method of decorating the black wares. Pueblo pottery is slipped and rubbed to achieve a burnished effect. Julian discovered that painting the burnished pot with slip would produce a design consisting of the contrast between dull, or matte, and the shiny surface of the burnished ware. And the artist in him was then able to completely reverse his prior painting technique to paint in the backgrounds of the desired design, thus presenting the figures as glossy and the background as matte.

After Julian's death, Maria worked with her son Popovi Da and with Santana, both of whom became well-known potters in their own right.

The present collection contains works of Maria (380, 381), Maria and Santana (382-383) and of Santana (384). It is also of some interest to note that the production of pottery by Pueblo Indians was almost a thing of the past until stimulated by the interest of archeologists and the appreciation of its aesthetic qualities by persons who were eager to invest in its production.

Pueblo basketry resembles the pottery in a number of ways. The shapes remain plain and graceful, the decorations geometric designs or stylized life forms, and the colors are generally rather soft. Coiling was, again, a common form of manufacture (see, for example 474-477), though other techniques were also used (477-480). With the exception of the Hopi, the art of basketry is rare among Pueblo Indians today.

Prehistoric Pueblo Indians made mosaics using bone, shell and local stones such as turquoise. The technique was adapted to jewelry, as illustrated by the necklace (447). The same basic technique is in use today in the form of inlays set in silver by the Zuni, to form rings and pins and bracelets. In the present exhibit are examples of the type of jewelry made by Pueblo Indians before the introduction of European tools and metal techniques (442-446).

The pump drill (503) was used in boring holes in bone and shell. A versatile implement, it was also used (without the drill point) to generate fire by twirling the wooden shaft rapidly in a hole in a wooden plank.

Much of the artistic work of the Pueblo Indians revolved around their religious beliefs. On the walls of their underground *kivas* (religious rooms) they painted murals in the same general style as the paintings of the early twentieth century painters exhibited here. The subjects of the *kiva* murals tended to be representative of the spirits (or *kachinas*) who were both ancestral to living things and also helped the people by maintaining the earth and its products. As part of their religious worship, Pueblo Indians paid homage to the gods—and celebrated life—through prayers, songs and dances, in which *kachinas* appear in human form. Modern Pueblo paintings are still concerned with these important events.

The Corn Dance by Quah Ah (404), The Comanche Dance by Pan Yo Pin (413) and the Ceremonial Dance by Oqwa Pi (405) are all representative examples. Painting on paper with water colors was a new medium to the Indians of the Southwest. It was a technique that was stimulated by the school environment and encouraged by teachers as well as anthropologists, and to which, once again, the Indian brought his own uniqueness.

As an art form, southwestern Indian paintings began to be

produced about 1917. The present exhibition includes works of most of the noteworthy early painters, including Awa Tsireh considered by some to be one of the founders of this "school" of painting (410-412), Fred Kabotie (400), Richard Martinez (407), Oqwa Pi (406), Pan Yo Pin (413), and Quah Ah (401-404). Since most of the southwestern painters were male, Quah Ah, who was female, is of particular note. Further, it might interest the viewer to note that The Deer Dance (408) was painted by the same Julian Martinez who is referred to above in connection with the development of the San Ildefonso black ware and its decoration.

Weaponry is noticeably scarce in the Pueblo materials, particularly when compared to their neighbors, the Plains Indians. An interesting hunting implement, however, is the throwing stick (507) which the Pueblo Indian used in hunting rabbits. With a bit more curve to it, the Hopi would have shared with the Australian aborigine the distinction of having invented the boomerang.

Navajo culture is composed of a number of elements derived from diverse sources. The Navajo entered the southwest in prehistoric times (about 500 years ago) as wandering hunters who also gathered wild plant foods. By the time they were first contacted by the Spanish, they had already adopted a number of culture traits from the Pueblos. Most significant of these, perhaps, was the custom of planting corn. During the Pueblo rebellion against the Spanish (1680 to 1692) a number of Pueblo Indians took refuge among the Navajo. At this time, the Navajo adopted a number of additional traits of Pueblo culture, including the weaving of fabrics and the absorption of many aspects of Pueblo religion. To all of these, however, the Navajo brought their own particular flavor. The weaving, for example, was applied to wool rather than cotton and was practiced by women rather than men.

The Spanish also contributed a number of significant influences on the Navajo, most notably the introduction of the horse and of sheep. With sheep to herd, and the horse to use in doing so, the Navajo developed the pattern of living in small hamlets, raising corn and herding sheep.

The sheep provided not only food but also the fiber with which the Navajos created their own particular variety of textile: the Navajo blanket. By the early eighteenth century Navajos were weaving wool fabrics for use as shoulder coverings and, in the form of two such blankets sewn together, for women's dresses (430). The production of textiles was, therefore, a relatively new and utilitarian endeavor among them. The early colors were confined to the natural shades of wool, plus native dyes of black, yellow, green and red hues, and the Spanish-introduced indigo blue. Designs consisted of horizontal bands of color. An example of this early type of blanket is shown (416).

The superior quality of Navajo blankets was recognized early in the southwest, where they became popular items of trade with other Indians and with Mexicans. However, the production of blankets as a major activity among the Navajo did not occur until the last decade of the nineteenth century, at which time traders became interested in them for American markets. Interestingly, Fred Harvey (of Harvey Houses associated with the Santa Fe railroad) was very instrumental in popularizing the Navajo blankets, marketing them and helping to maintain their quality.

The American market brought about a change in the textiles, which is reflected in the phrase "Navajo rug". The buyer desired the Navajo's art as a floor covering, and the Navajo accommodated him by weaving a larger product and incorporating design, including borders, that pleased the purchaser. Triangles and other designs involving diagonal lines became popular, and finally the inclusion of animal and plant designs. With the larger spaces to work in, more variation in dyes, non-Indian

416

textiles for inspiration, and income to be derived from the work put into their manufacture, the Navajo created a distinctive form of textile art.

A particularly interesting blanket in this display is the rare "two-faced" blanket (415), a style invented about 1890 but never widely manufactured. This blanket is woven in one piece, with the two differing designs front and back being created simultaneously by the weaver as she works—a real testimony to the skill of the weaver.

Like the blankets, silver work by the Navajo is a relatively recent development, and also like the blankets, the Navajo brought to this new medium a unique quality. In the middle of the nineteenth century a Navajo man, named Atsidi Sani, learned to work silver in Mexico and brought the process back to Arizona. For a time he made items for his own use and that of his friends and kinsmen. And from him, his sons and friends learned the art. The early products of the silversmiths were bells, buttons, buckles, bracelets and beads, utilizing coins and other forms of alloyed silver, without the addition of turquoise. They were items made for their own use and for trade with Pueblo Indians.

Once again, the encouragement of this as an art form, and the stimulus for its further development, came about as a result of the development of an American market. And, also again, the Harvey Houses were involved. For by the end of the nineteenth century, the Harvey Houses were purchasing silver work for sale to the tourists. It was an employee of the Harvey chain, Herman Schweizer, who, about 1899, introduced to the Navajo the idea of setting turquoise in the silver jewelry to make it more attractive to the tourist. The American market, further, initially desired silver ornaments that were less heavy than what the Navajo had made for his own use. So whereas the American Market had resulted in larger Navajo blankets, it contrarily resulted in finer and more delicate Navajo silver pieces.

We tend to associate the concha belt (440-441) specifically with the Navajo. It is of some interest to realize that the working of the silver is of Mexican introduction, the use of a belt depends upon the Euro-Asiatic trousers, the concha design was adopted by the Navajo from the Plains tribes, and the use of turquoise in the concha was due to the influence of an American railroad employee. And yet, as an examination of the silver jewelry (454-460) will show, the Navajo brought his own distinctive touch to this combination.

Before leaving the Southwest, a word on the Apache is in order. Like the Navajo, they were recent hunting and gathering migrants to the area prehistorically, and they acquired the art of raising corn from the Pueblos. Though they did not become weavers of textiles or silversmiths, their basketry is quite distinctive for the Southwest. Utilizing the coiling process primarily, their decorative techniques of repetitive figures (462-465, 469, 472) make them easily recognizable as Apache.

Summary

The American Indian was the first human being to inhabit the North American continent. He brought relatively little with him from Asia, and much of what he brought was not applicable to non-arctic areas. Nevertheless, he developed on this "other side of the world" new and exciting ways of dealing with the world. Many of the items he invented to enable his adjustment have been lost to the contemporary world. But some have remained for our appreciation . . . and the appreciation of his direct descendents.

> Beth Dillingham, PhD
> Associate Professor of Anthropology,
> University of Cincinnati

Bibliography

Adair, John, *The Navajo and Pueblo Silversmiths.* Univ. of Okla. Press, Norman, 1944.

Amsden, Charles Avery, *Navajo Weaving: Its Technic and its History.* The Rio Grande Press, Inc., Glorieta, New Mexico, 1974.

Dunn, Dorothy, *American Indian Painting of the Southwest and Plains Areas.* Univ. of New Mexico Press, Albuquerque, 1968.

Marriott, Alice, *Maria: The Potter of San Ildefonso.* U. of Okla. Press, Norman, 1948.

Hatt, Gudmund, "Moccasins and Their Relation to Arctic Footwear" Memoir of the American Anthropological Association, Vol III, 1916.

Newcomb, William W., Jr., *North American Indians: An Anthropological Perspective.* Goodyear Publishing Co., Pacific Palisades, Calif., 1974.

James, George Wharton, *Indian Basketry.* Dover Publications, Inc., New York, 1972.

Drucker, Philip, *Indians of the Northwest Coast.* Natural History Press, Garden City, N.Y., 1963.

Lowie, Robert H., *Indians of the Plains.* Natural History Press, Garden City, N.Y., 1963.

Kroeber, Alfred L., *Handbook of the Indians of California.* Bureau of American Ethnology Bulletin 78, Washington, D.C., 1925.

The Ancient Midwest—
Twelve Thousand Years

American archaeology has been a subject of scholarly pursuit for two hundred years and in the Ohio Valley since the late 1700's. The downtown Cincinnati area had a number of burial mounds and ceremonial enclosures which were located from Second to Thirteen Streets and from Mound Street to Pike and Lytle. Some of the oldest and most famous finds in that early period were made in the Cincinnati area. Both European and then American commentators were interested in the question of the origin of the American Indian and of the connection if any between the historic Indian groups and the archaeological remains found so abundantly in this country. Handicapped as they were by inaccurate concepts of the age of the world and of man, they reached some rather unfortunate conclusions.

One of the major mistakes was the belief that the Indians were a separate and distinct group from the preceding Mound Builders who were much more advanced culturally and had been driven out and exterminated by the savage Indians. Another persistent attitude was that any significant or worthwhile cultural development must have been brought in by people from the Mediterranean basin, northern Europe, or as a last resort, from known Asiatic cultures. Today professional archaeologists universally reject these proposals with very few exceptions.

There has been a long slow growth of reliable data and interpretations of American Archaeology but now there is a very large specialized literature. At present we have a reliable temporal framework, a clear succession of culture changes from early to late, almost all moving gradually toward increasing cultural complexity and the production of more and more items of material culture.

Much of the prehistoric material in this exhibition is the product of past Indian populations of the Cincinnati area and of nearby areas in the midwest. It honors their achievements in their occupation of this land for at least twelve thousand years. We do not know the languages they spoke or the names of their social and political units, except perhaps for some reasonable hypotheses where we can connect the most like occupants of the central Ohio Valley to the late prehistoric and early historic sites.

Archaeologists have divided Ohio Valley prehistory and that of the Eastern United States into a number of rather arbitrary time units. It is not known for certain when the first human groups moved from northeast Asia into North America on the great Beringia land platform, nor when the first people arrived in the Ohio Valley. It is reasonably certain that Indian ancestors were in America some 20,000 years ago and that they were in the Ohio Valley by about 12,000 years ago. This early period is called Paleo-Indian and may be said to last from the first appearance of these early hunters until about 10,000 years ago. Quite recently excavations by the University of Pittsburgh at the Meadowcroft rock shelter southwest of Pittsburgh have produced radiocarbon dates of around 16,500 years ago said to be associated with flint knives, flakes, scrapers and other tools of flint.

The best known artifacts of the Paleo-Indian complexes are the projectile points, spear and knife forms known as "fluted" points (509-520). This type or style of point is recognized by its general narrow lanceolate shape and the removal of longitudinal flakes from the base toward the tip of the point. Since their first identification with now extinct bison species near Folsom, New Mexico, in the late 1920's one variant has been called a Folsom point, while another, somewhat older, larger and with much shorter fluting, is named Clovis after another find area near Clovis, New Mexico. In the eastern United States and the central Ohio Valley there are very few specifically Folsom points, for most of the thousands of fluted forms in the east most closely resemble the Clovis style. Also in the east there are many specializations, recognizable by experts, which reflect individual craftmanship or the product of small group traditions of the correct way to shape a point.

In the High Plains of the United States these fluted points have been found with a variety of extinct fauna. Organic material from the deposits have been consistently dated within a time period of 9400 to 8000 B.C. There has also been uncovered additional artifact material and some excavations have been made at former habitation sites so that a better interpretation of their way of life may be obtained than from most of the sites in the east. Most of our eastern data comes from early private collecting, and there have been very few systematic pick-ups from former camp settlements and very few controlled and reported excavations. The most extensive excavations have been in Nova Scotia and near London, Ontario, on the northern and northeastern fringes of the distribution of this style.

In the eastern United States while there is strong evidence of the contemporaneity of man, mastodon, caribou, an extinct beaver form and the peccary, no indisputable evidence of direct hunting or other association has been obtained. We do know that these earliest hunters had occupied the entire area from the Gulf states to the Laurentians. The climatic pattern was still in process of adjustment from that which produced the melting of the glacial ice in the United States. That vegetational patterns were quite different is indicated by strong components of the boreal forest such as spruce and pine which had formerly moved quite far south along the Appalachians and in the upland areas west of the Mississippi.

516, 519, 510, 511

Close study of lithic debris at Paleo-Indian sites in the United States has resulted in the recognition of at least four different types of sites. One is an area close by a source of lithic material for their tools and implements which produces large hammerstones, quarry blocks and rejects, almost finished items and much debris. Another type of site is a base camp near one or more quarry areas where normal daily living activities took place, shelters were erected, and tools and implements were put into final form. Game animals have rather regular feeding and other activity patterns so that once learned man could locate his hunting camps in areas that were near trails or favored feeding areas at specific times of the year. They also rapidly learned the most favorable location for and time of fruiting of the various nuts, seeds and berries that were added to the diet. A fourth type of site, known more in the west than the east, is a processing station where large game animals were butchered. Yearly settlement activity would have been of small bands of closely related folk, moving slowly from one favorable hunting and collecting area to another.

Because of climatic conditions only the lithic tool remain from this period. Besides the projectile points, knives and spears, there were flint scrapers for working skins, flint flakes with small sharp graving points, chisel-like points, bone awls, needles and beads, and heavy flint scrapers, planes and choppers. Part of their clothing was furnished by animal skins, and the skeletal parts furnished other tools. They must also have worked and utilized wood for shelter, containers and implements as well as for fire.

Early Archaic

The fluted points are such a distinctive style that their gradual disappearance may be used to separate the first major known occupations from the beginning of a long period of gradual cultural growth with slow incremental exploitation of the environment. This long period from about 8000 B.C. to 1000 B.C. is called the Archaic and can be divided into three sub-periods. The Early Archaic from about 8000 to 6000 B.C. produced a much greater variety of point and knife forms which were developed gradually, perhaps in response to a wide variety of more specific tasks for such tools and to the development of minor modifications of the attachment of the point to a handle or shaft. The basic flint and stone industry is carried on as before with the addition of such important tools as sandstone abraders or cobbles for grinding vegetables on mortar stones. Probably the most important new tool was the chipped flint adze primarily for heavy wood working. This became an important industrial tool over a wide area and could have been used to make dugout canoes and bowls, and to trim trees for shelter construction and so on.

The Beaver Lake type of point (530) is named after a lake in northern Alabama and represents a form believed to be only slightly later than the fluted point. The Agate Basin type (551, 552) is named after a location in southeastern Wyoming where this form was associated with extinct bison. The Dalton form (539, 540) was named for a prominent amateur archaeologist and Supreme Court Justice in Missouri. The Thebes type (553) was named for a town in southern Illinois and the Kirk forms (543-550) were first defined in North Carolina. This is a reflection of the wide spread adoption of point styles as small band groups would come into contact with each other at favorable hunting, collecting or gathering localities. By such contacts raw materials and exotic specimens were able to move over considerable distances.

There are some flint deposits which because of their color or other features can be recognized as originating in specific areas. East of Newark, Ohio, a very famous deposit is known as Flint Ridge; deposits of nodular bluish grey flint from southern Indiana is called Harrison County. There are also distinctive quarry locations of black flint in the Upper Mercer formations of Eastern Ohio and in the Kanawha Valley or the distinctive dark brownish banded flint from near Dover, Tennessee. Both in the Paleo-Indian and Early Archaic period there is evidence of long distance transport of individual tools and implements, and also of raw material. This practice continued up to the historic period.

The first indication of a specific area set aside for burial is known from a Dalton site in northeastern Arkansas where some twelve graves were located at some distance from a habitation site. Artifact material included carefully made and essentially unused tools and implements. Another burial site in eastern Wisconsin has the first recorded presence of powdered red ocher placed with a burial.

By the Early Archaic Period the vegetation and animal life in much of the Ohio Valley were probably similar to those of the early historic period. Indian life was adjusted to a woodland, riverine economy. A wide variety of game, some fish and birds, nuts, seeds and berries were eaten. We do not know very much of their vegetal intake. There are, however, indications from the increase in the number and size of known sites of this period and the greater number and variety of implements that there was a population increase. There are better indications from details of tool forms and the normal predominance of local resources for their manufacture that the populations were confining most of their activities to relatively restricted band territories, moving about from location to loca-

529, 553, 530, 543, 531, 552, 540

tion with the change of the seasons and the availability of food. It is also believed that at times a number of related bands would gather near a favorable area such as a grove of nut producing trees and interact with social and religious observances. Group performance and behavior almost certainly was guided by the experienced elders.

Middle Archaic

This period recognizes the development and introduction of a number of new tools and implements. At some time between 6000 and 4000 B.C. the full-grooved stone axe made its first appearance (567) although it became much more common in the next period. It is likely that this wood working tool used with short chopping strokes, as was the adze, was developed from the earlier chipped adze form. This was but one of the ground and polished stone forms that appeared during the period, for the eastern Indians were developing these skills before the possibility of introduction of such a concept from outside the area. Many of the projectile points were attached to short dart shafts four to five feet long which were propelled by a spear thrower or atlatl, to use the Aztec word. Grave finds indicate very clearly that for many centuries the hunters placed a polished stone artifact on the cylindrical shaft of the spear thrower. These so-called bannerstones (568) were given a wide variety of forms and sizes and were made from many different materials. They were drilled by means of a hollow tube and sand, either by hand or with a bow drill. There were also small pendants of stone made of flat ovoid pebbles and perforated near the apex by a drilled hole.

There is more evidence available from rock shelters where conditions were favorable for bone preservation. We know that bone fishhooks, antler tip projectile points, antler handles, a large variety of bone awls, perforators and scrapers were employed for working skins and there is some evidence of the production of mats and perhaps baskets from vegetal material.

In the Cincinnati Art Museum four projectile point types are selected to represent this period. They are the LeCroy point first named from finds in western Tennessee but with an almost continent-wide distribution (558-560); Eva, another form named for a locality in western Tennessee along the Tennessee River (561); Lost Lake from northern Alabama (566); and Kanawha Stemmed, named after a deep site on the Kanawha Valley, West Virginia (556-557). These are simply representative of the increasing use of flint and of shifting styles of point manufacture.

Few burials have been found, but most of them were in a flexed or fetal position and they were placed in small excavated pits. Some dogs were carefully buried; they are known in the east by around 6000 B.C. and were even earlier in the western part of the continent. The human population from available skeletal material appears to have been relatively short and slender. They were rather long headed and had not begun to take on the various cranial modifications known from later times.

Among items which became of increasing importance in their diet were fresh water molluscs. The discarded shells provided eventually large refuse and midden heaps where burial remains and animal food remains are well preserved. Some burials are accompanied by burial goods which are usually personal utilitarian possessions. There are relatively few ornamental items such as beads, necklaces, bracelets or insignia. It is most common for the burials to be without recoverable grave furniture.

Late Archaic

The last division of the Archaic lasted from about 4000 to 1500 B.C. It appears to have had a considerable population growth and had considerable regional diversity from coastal ways of life to lake and river adapted populations and from the Mississippi flood plain area to the Appalachians. It reflects a significant increase in interregional trade such as large and small ocean shells from the Atlantic and Gulf Coast, and the discovery and utilization of Lake Superior copper initially for implements and later over a wide area for ornaments. The ocean shells reached as far into the interior as western Minnesota, and the copper was distributed from the Plains to New England and south as far as Florida. The distribution of copper tools and unworked copper pieces along the water routes of the Great Lakes to St. Lawrence is a good indicator that the birchbark canoe was probably in use at this time.

Additional ground and polished stone items made their appearance. A great many bannerstone forms (619-628) were

563, 557, 559, 561, 568

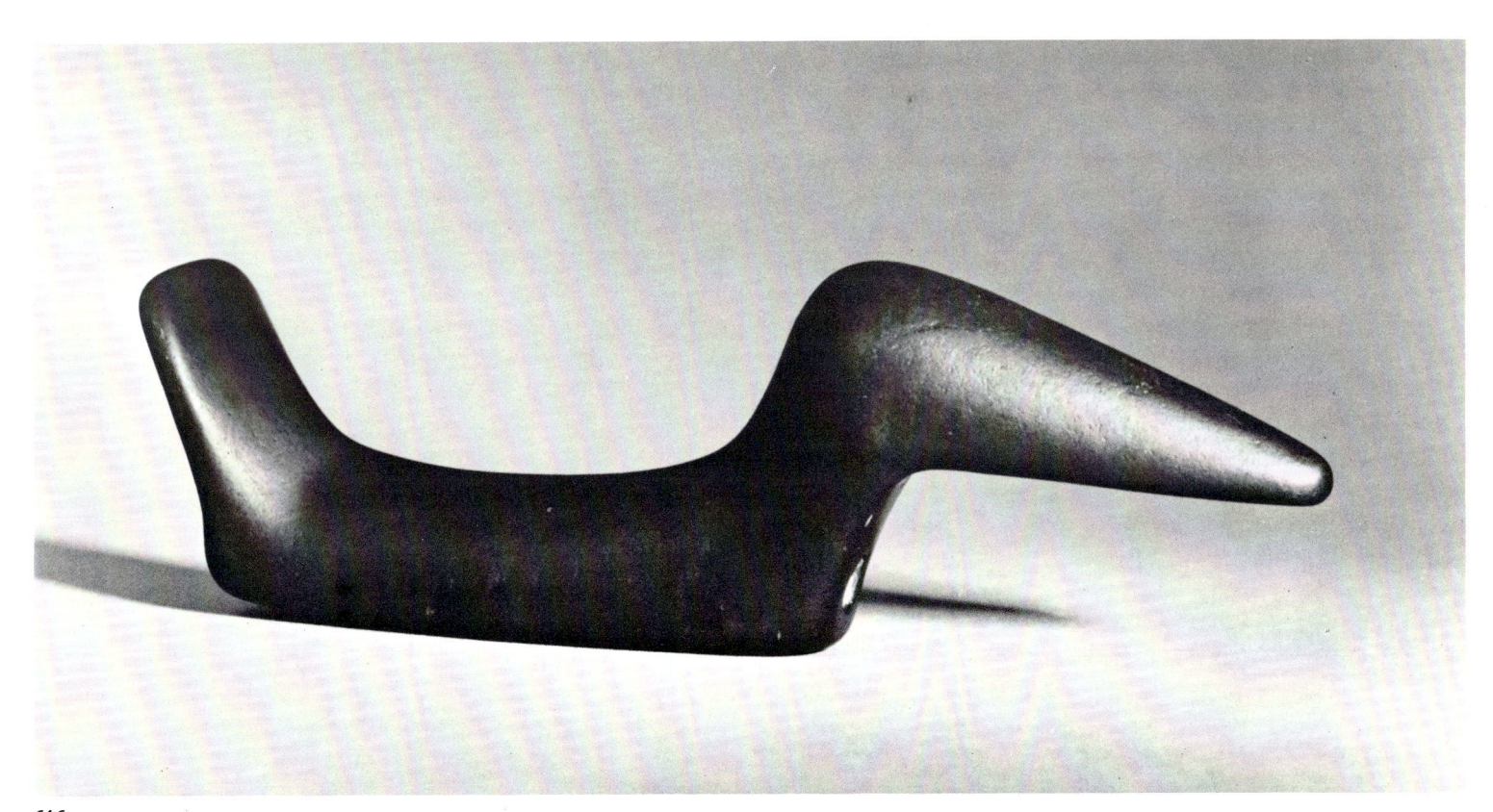

616

developed in different regions but toward the end of the period they were replaced by another distinctive form known as a birdstone (616). This shape is most common in the Great Lakes and Upper Ohio Valley. The bannerstone seems to have been replaced in the south primarily by the boat stone (656) in the next period. A great many ornamental forms were made of a distinctive blue gray slate into gorgets (577, 587) toward the end of the period. The so-called bell pestle (571-572), or the conical pestle, and roller pestle (573) were used with a mortar to grind seeds or other vegetal foods and are found in considerable numbers in the mid-south. The full-grooved axe was gradually replaced by the three-quarter grooved form (607-609) and eventually by a number of ungrooved axe or celt forms.

One of the new introductions by 2000 to 1500 B.C. was the tubular pipe of stone (570). We do not know what material was smoked, for the Indians smoked quite a variety of dried substances. It is however the earliest indication of pipe smoking. Stone plummets were added to the inventory and were employed attached to the periphery of nets to ensnare water birds. Some number of these in the central Mississippi Valley are made of hematite and these also were traded to a minor degree. Many flat bilaterally notched stones are recovered which are identified as net-sinkers. Stone bowls were manu-

factured from steatite quarries in the Appalachians from New England to Alabama, and from sandstone in northern Alabama. These also entered into the trade or exchange activity for examples of them are known from Ohio to the St. Louis area and into eastern Louisiana and Florida.

Another container was developed in the lower Savannah River and St. Johns River area of Georgia and Florida. Fiber tempered pottery bowl forms with plain inner and outer surfaces are known in both areas between 2500 and 2000 B.C. While some archaeologists believe this concept was brought in from the Colombia coast it does not appear likely for it is the only significant new form introduced at the same time and could well have been invented in the southeast. In any event it is by far the oldest pottery in North America.

Two projectile points chosen to illustrate forms of this period are the Godar and Hemphill forms (594, 589), both of the St. Louis area but many others are representative of different times and areas within this long period. The Cincinnati Art Museum has a large number of points representing this period in the Ohio Valley. This reflects a considerable population increase and a greater stability of occupation at preferred seasonal sites. This conclusion is reached partly because of the depth of occupation of some of the sites and also because of the marked increase in the number of burials that have been recovered and can be attributed to the Late Archaic.

The numerous bone awls and spatula shaped forms are regarded as mute evidence of mat, basket and early cloth production, the latter made from native bast fibers. The bone flute and whistle appear and along with rattles of turtle shell are the earliest identified musical instruments.

Many of the village sites have baking, steaming or roasting pits which were used for mussel shells, meats or tubers and roots. There are also post-hole patterns left in the ground from former circular and rectangular structures unfortunately not too clearly described yet from Midwestern sites.

By this time the several Indian societies had achieved considerable competence in a variety of tasks. Game was collected by spear, dart, nets, hooks, fish weirs in streams, and almost certainly by traps and snares. At the time of the arrival of European explorers in the Great Lakes area the Indians were using 130 species of plants for food, but even more remarkable was their herbal medicine kit of 275 species, 31 as magical charms, 27 for smoking, 25 to make dyes, 18 for beverages and flavoring, and 52 for sundry utilitarian purposes. A considerable number of these were almost certainly known in Late Archaic times and in good harvest and hunting times could have provided a rather well balanced diet.

One of the more intriguing developments was the discovery and utilization of the pure native copper in formations on and close to the surface in the Isle Royale to Keweenaw peninsula area. From roughly 3000 B.C. to the 17th century these deposits were worked by hammering the native rock away from the copper veins, nuggets, or even considerable boulder size pieces. Thousands of pits have been found where the prehistoric miners used glacial and beach cobbles as hammerstones. By hammering and heating they worked this strange malleable "stone" into utilitarian knives, spear, awls, fishhooks, harpoons and other forms similar to those in stone and bone with which they were already familiar. The greatest concentration of these Old Copper tools is in the eastern half of Wisconsin, adjoining Michigan and Ontario.

Most of the burials were in a flexed position but other burial procedures were also observed such as bundle burials where only skeletal parts were present at interment, extended, and cremation. Burials were placed most often adjacent to or in a village midden. Often they are in former cooking or refuse pits. While some amount of care was usually displayed in the interment in many cases it appears to have been done hurriedly or casually. Later groups would often disperse an earlier burial to inter a contemporary one. Indications of accidents, trauma, knife cuts and death through violence are not uncommon. Groups of tools or weapons seem to have been placed in containers in the grave and represent the possessions of craftsmen or hunters, and sometimes look like the assortment of items associated with a medicine bundle.

The Late Archaic populations, like most prehistoric and other groups before the development of modern medicine and sanitation had a low average life span of about 27 years. They suffered as they grew older from arthritis, extreme tooth wear and resulting abcesses, rickets in children, bladder and kidney stones, and some examples of bone involvement which might possibly be from syphilis. Some of the middens in the Kentucky area have contained over 1200 burials, and many other sites have had burial counts well up in the hundreds. Close study of these tells us that most of the people from such cemeteries were closely related genetically, that there are minor variations from location to location and through time but that the dominant physical type was still the relatively short, slender, long headed population which was in the area earlier and which survived, particularly in the peripheral Woodland areas up to the historic period.

This period also marks the major development in the increase of ornamentation for individuals in the form of beads made from mussel and imported marine shell (639-643) in shell pendants and hair pins, engraved bone awls with rectilinear or curvilinear patterns which have been recovered from northern Alabama, the Georgia coast, Indiana and Illinois. We do not know what art forms were produced in wood or on skins. Many of these cited examples were placed with burials for they were the personal belongings of the individual and in some cases may be symbolic of his role in the society. Some of the grave goods appear to have been specifically made to accompany the deceased for there are no signs of other use but in other cases worn and even broken artifacts were included.

Early Woodland

Between 1500 B.C. and 1000 B.C., a number of additions were made to the cultural complexes of the several societies. Not all of them were universally adopted but some of the important ones did cover a considerable portion of the east. Burial mounds gradually become a distinctive part of the burial process. They are of earth and range in size from less than a foot high and 15 to 20 feet in diameter to impressive structures, such as the Miamisburg mound, some 68 feet high and 250 feet in diameter that were constructed toward the end of the early Woodland period about 200 B.C. Burial mounds are known from lower Canada to the Gulf and from the Eastern Plains to the Atlantic Coast. They are almost certainly a development within that area for they are not known in Mexico, western or northern Canada, Alaska, or in northeast Asia. They may occur singly or in groups, near or on a village site, or on top of uplands overlooking a valley. They received the remains of single or multiple burials. In some cases they probably represent family groups within a short or longer time, or even a series of individuals who probably represent prominent individuals and their immediate kin over a long period of time. The famous Serpent Mound in Adams County, Ohio, is near a number of Adena burial mounds and village site material and is believed to be Adena.

Disposal of the dead took a number of forms but particularly in the central Ohio Valley many of the adult burials of the Adena culture were extended, and some were in carefully prepared log tombs. Many individuals were cremated, and bundle and flexed positions are also known. Some individuals were buried with considerable caches of either finished or almost finished tools which were placed with the dead or sometimes in areas without other occupational evidence. Many of the best objects of material culture that have been preserved have been obtained with burials and they are our best guide to the striking skills of the Indian craftsmen.

Fiber tempered bowl manufacture slowly spread across the southeast to the Mississippi Valley and as far north as northern Alabama. Knowledge of the ability to produce baked clay containers appears to have diffused northward where the earliest crude grit-tempered bowl or flower-pot shaped vessels are known from shortly before 1500 B.C. These vessels instead of being constructed by modelling were made by adding ropes or coils of prepared clay to a basal section until the desired height was produced. During the Early Woodland period the vessel surfaces were paddled with a cordwrapped paddle or had other simple exterior treatment. Decoration was only used during the latter part of the period as the potters' skills improved.

Probably the most important new developments were the first attempts at agriculture in the east. Squash and gourds which were domesticated before 5000 B.C. in Mexico were apparently taken into the Southwest and from there reached the Kentucky area by about 1000 B.C. They have been identified in rock shelters and in caves in Kentucky. Dessicated bodies remarkably preserved have been carefully dissected for evidence of food remains. These studies and those of other evidence of food has produced the seeds and radiocarbon dates. By 500 B.C. squash was being grown in northwestern Ohio and in Michigan. In addition two of the native seed products, sunflower and sumpweed *(Iva annua var. macrocarpa)* appear to have been domesticated. The sunflower was destined to spread widely in the United States and had an international market. It is not clear whether the domestication of the local plants began before or after the introduction of the idea from outside the area, and the introduction of the tropical plants may be considerably earlier. In any event the percentage of cultivated to wild plants and other foods was very low.

Many of the items from the Ohio Valley in the exhibition and in the collections of the Museum belong to a cultural unit called Adena after the name of the estate of Governor Thomas Worthington near Chillicothe. The largest mound on that site has been regarded as the type mound for this complex. The majority of the burial mounds are found in the Central Ohio Valley from southeastern Indiana to southwestern Pennsylvania and from the Kentucky Blue Grass area to just north of the Indianapolis-Columbus-Pittsburgh line. Their number must have been up in the thousands. The Adena Complex people began to build mounds around 500 B.C. They were the descendants of the older Late Archaic populations. They had undergone some modification in cranial morphology partially as the result of cradle flattening of the back of the infant's head as it was bound to the board and partially perhaps to change in diet.

The basic stone implement assemblage and the tasks performed remained essentially unchanged but there were modifications in projectile styles and forms such as the Adena point (752) in the early Adena sites and the Robbins' point (755) in the late Adena locations which are representative. A distinctive form with several variants is known as the "turkey-tail" (745). While these are known from some Adena mounds they are most common in Ohio, Indiana, Illinois, Wisconsin, and Michigan. They are sometimes associated in groups with burials or in large caches. The turkey tails are normally made from a bluish gray nodular flint which is known from formations in southern Indiana, Illinois and northern Kentucky. Most of the specimens in Indiana and Ohio may well have been quarried from the southern Indiana deposits, but the Illinois deposits probably contributed to those in that state, Wisconsin and Michigan.

During Early Woodland times there was a shift in the use of copper from primarily utilitarian to ornamental forms. In the Adena Culture, particularly in its later years, the artisans made gorgets, crescents and bracelets (675-678) which were placed with a small number of the deceased who occupied positions of leadership in the community. Copper beads continue to be made and for a short time in late Adena there were finger rings. Copper celts and adzes (660-662) and copper awls were produced. The celts and adzes placed with the dead seldom have signs of use. This is the first significant use of copper in the Central Ohio Valley. The exact way in which it was obtained is not known but the copper does represent a continuation and accentuation of long standing trade and exchange activity.

The full-grooved axe disappeared and was replaced by the

three-quarter grooved form and the celt (609, 654). Boatstones are associated with the throwing stick. Slate pendants and gorgets (679-692) were made in considerable numbers in the Ohio-Indiana area and were occasionally traded into the south and west. The expanded-center and quadriconcave-sided gorget are typical of Adena burial furniture. The first significant use of mica to make crescents or other ornamental forms appears at this time in Adena burials. The mica was obtained from deposits in Western North Carolina.

Many tubular pipes were made from a fine-grained siltstone which occurs in south-central Ohio just north of the Ohio River. The pipes became much more cylindrical (No. 657) and some had modifications of the bit which blocked the tube's contents from entering the mouth. In some areas where suitable stone was not obtainable, like the lower Mississippi Valley and New England, pipes were made of baked clay. There was considerable trade of the Ohio made pipes particularly into the Mid-Atlantic area of Delaware and Chesapeake Bay where they may have been exchanged for marine shells. A few tubular effigy pipes were sculptured to represent a duck, especially the neck and bead of the shoveller duck. One of the finest examples of American Indian sculpture is the famous Adena pipe in the Ohio State Historical Society which presents a dwarf-like figure in a bent-knee position wearing copper ear spools, a breech cloth and an elaborate headdress. It was found in the main mound on Gov. Worthington's estate.

One of the distinctive features of a few of the late Adena mounds in Kentucky and Ohio is the presence of small engraved or incised baked clay or stone tablets. A few have circular or other geometric patterns but the majority have highly conventionalized representations of a hooked beak or raptorial bird. Some of these designs look like models for ones placed on pottery in the next period. A number of circular bone gorgets taken from an adult human skull cap were placed with burials and one of these from near Florence, Ohio, had an engraved raptorial bird design on it. Some of the decorated and some undecorated stone tablets have rather small depressions on their reverse side which was used to grind red ocher into a powder to obtain red paint.

The Cincinnati Art Museum has one of the rare engraved tablets which has been largely ignored by contemporary archaeologists although it has been in the Museum since 1890 and was illustrated in two earlier publications. It is known as the Waverly tablet (666) and was found by a farmer who was levelling his field in Pike County, Ohio, in 1872. It resembles but is not as well done as the famous Cincinnati Tablet belonging to the Cincinnati Historical Society which was found in the large tumulus at Fifth and Mound Streets that was truncated by Mad Anthony Wayne to construct an observation platform.

The pottery associated with late Adena sites was thinner, had smaller tempering particles and was better fired than earlier products. The outer surface was plain except in a few rare examples of rectilinear incising on the rim and upper body area. While there are regional variations the similarity is so great that it bespeaks for relatively easy movement of at least some people and of ideas from one river valley to another.

Adena houses were normally circular and varied in size from small single family to multiple-family structures which could have held up to 40 people. Many Adena mounds were built over former structures following one or more deaths and the interments took place within the dwelling which was then burned. Village size varied from a few houses to larger villages with 10 or more structures. In the interior there was a central hearth and various pits for storage but no indication of partitions dividing the area into family units or specific work areas. The people probably did not occupy their villages the year round. While the increased number of sites and material from Early Woodland sites again indicates a population increase there would still have been less than one per square mile. The use of a single word "Adena" to encompass the large number of sites and the length of time involved implies a unity that it did not have. It should not be regarded as a political unit, a single language group or a cohesive restricted "society." Instead it was composed of quite different bands in different parts of river valleys with their composition changing through time and with periods of individual and group contact with neighboring bands. It is also possible that individuals or small groups of men engaged in long distance trade and acquisition of some of the exotic items that were incorporated into their cultural complex.

657, 662, 656, 663, 654

666

Middle Woodland

The next prehistoric temporal unit widely recognized is dominated by the Hopewell culture of Ohio and related Hopewellian societies in the mid-continent area from the Gulf of Mexico into lower Michigan and Wisconsin. In every era gradual change and development took place but during this period we can see the exchange and aquisition of both raw materials and finished items on a scale not known before and perhaps equalled but not surpassed during the last major culture period before the arrival of the Europeans. The name Hopewell is derived from that of the owner of a farm west of Chillicothe, Ohio, in 1890-91 which was partially excavated by Warren K. Moorehead of Xenia, Ohio, at the request of the Director of the Peabody Museum at Harvard University who was organizing the acquisition of materials for the World's Columbian Exposition in Chicago. Some part of the collection is still at the Field Museum. The Cincinnati Art Museum Collection is largely from surface material and does not have the more spectacular excavated material.

Some number of late Adena sites are composed of earth wall circles with an interior ditch and a single entryway. Some of these are still preserved, notably in the city cemetery in Marietta, Ohio, and this has a burial mound within the circle. The production of ceremonial earthworks continued in south-central and southwestern Ohio and large complex geometric circles, squares, octagons, parallel walls, "forts" and irregular shapes were constructed. These constructions varied in size from small squares enclosing a few acres to large complex groups connected by walled pathways as at Newark, Ohio, where close to 200 acres were enclosed in the several earthworks. The earthworks were built to enclose mound groups, village sites and for ceremonial activities such as dances and games. Some of them may have had timber walls but this has not been demonstrated. The large ones were certainly built over a period of time perhaps a few hundred years. They are almost unique to Ohio and beside the group in what is now downtown Cincinnati, a large and famous group was located on the east side of the Little Miami River southeast of Cincinnati. This Turner group was excavated in the latter part of the last century and up to 1908 for the Peabody Museum at Harvard. Unfortunately this site has been destroyed by gravel operations.

The burial ceremonies and activities were more complex than they were in Early Woodland times. While many of the mounds were small, some of them at the major Ohio Hopewell sites were very large and contained hundreds of burials. Some of these mounds seem to have been built on top of former charnel houses where some portion of the deceased was kept before burial. Some of the mounds covered from one to five or six such structures and represent the passage of many years. Burials were predominantly cremated in many of the mounds, extended burials were present and many were accompanied by extensive grave goods reflecting their rank in the society and their possession or control of certain items. Distinctive prepared clay basins in some of the mounds received the burnt offerings of an incredible amount of ornamental and exotic material. Many of them contain the cremated remains of burials but some of the great caches of objects did not have skeletal material.

This period in the Central Ohio is the culmination of the long period of cultural development in the east in many ways. It had, as mentioned, the most complex earthwork and burial practices. It carried the interest in collecting exotic materials to a high level. The tendency to bury large numbers of specialized articles in mounds or in other areas reached seemingly absurd heights. The artistic capabilities of some of the craftsmen in stone, metal, clay, and bone art were unequalled. Hopewell art cannot be easily characterized except that almost all of it was involved one way or other with their concepts of the supernatural, the spirit world, and the forces which affect human life and destiny. It is almost certainly not art for art's sake for each piece seems clearly designed to belong to their conceptual framework of religious beliefs.

Much of the sculpture was of a new and predominant pipe form called the platform pipe (775). Many of these were made of Ohio pipestone but they also were made of limestone or other relatively soft stone. A high proportion of all of the platform pipes in Ohio were recovered from two large cremated caches at the Tremper site near Portsmouth which contained some 136 pipes both plain and effigy types, and the Mound City cache north of Chillicothe which contained some 200 pipes. The effigy pipes were sculptured representations in surprisingly lifelike and identifiable forms of birds, mammals, fish and occasionally of a human head. The male heads on the pipes have marks on the face representing scarification, tatooing or painted designs and the individual wears a headdress. Other naturalistic representations were in baked clay human figures. These are best known from the Turner site in Ohio and the Knight site in Illinois. The production of these small human figures primarily of adults was fairly wide spread and done in a common style with great individual variability of ability. The Knight mound figurines are certainly the best.

Most of the Hopewell art however was geometric or highly conventionalized representation of life forms such as the distinctive bird designs on pottery. This art canon was followed by local potters in Ohio, Illinois, the lower Mississippi Valley and the northwest coast of Florida. Fine line engraving on boatstones and other utilitarian objects added to their esthetic appeal. The magnificent control of this technique by Hopewell artisans in Ohio is perhaps best represented in the intricate engraved designs on human bone. From the downtown Cincinnati Mound group a human upper arm bone had an intricate representation of a carnivore while a human ulna and a femur from the Hopewell site had engravings representing the bear. Probably many other examples of engraved bone were lost by the ceremonial fires through which some passed and others to poor excavation or recovery techniques.

Thin copper sheets provided the material for gorgets (760-761) and for a variety of copper cut out and repoussé designs. Some of these forms include copper headdresses for males with cut out designs and positions for the attachment of pearls. The repoussé designs feature fish and bird effigies. Most of these items were for personal adornment for shamans and other male leaders of the society. Another exotic material that received somewhat similar treatment was mica which normally appears in mound burials in the form of fairly large sheets of 4 to 12 inches in diameter. Its reflective surface must have been regarded as possessing some special power. It was shaped into various forms such as spears, bear canines, eagle claw, human hand, human figure and various geometric forms.

The human figures have the same curious bent knee posture of the Adena effigy pipe and the clay figurines. Some of the repoussé designs in copper may possibly have been for stencils for painting designs on cloth.

One of the fine diagnostic products was the copper earspool (762-763) made in a number of variations in technique and form and sometimes combined with silver or meteoric iron. These are usually associated with male burials and are comparatively rare outside of southern Ohio. The Hopewell site itself was a major production center, for over two thousand were found at that site. Most of these had been fused into a large mass during a ceremonial fire. In all, well over five thousand copper objects were recovered from this site. Another unusual object of copper is believed to be a pan pipe with three or four reeds of different lengths enclosed within a thin copper sheath. Nine of these were from the Hopewell site. One of the first to be found was in the downtown village area of Cincinnati and another very early find was at Marietta. They are known from well over 30 sites from north of Lake Ontario, to Jacksonville, and from Mobile Bay to La Crosse, Wisconsin. Copper celts and adzes are even more widely distributed. They are usually with male burials and are regarded more as symbolic than utilitarian objects. There were thousands of copper beads and a few bracelets and rings. The copper salts preserved some of the textiles, bark, hair, hide and feathers in which they were wrapped before being put in the grave. The eastern Indians used Indian hemp *(Apocinum cannabinum),* swamp milkweed *(Asclepias incarnata),* rabbit fur and the inner bark of trees such as linden, slippery elm, and some other plants to manufacture thread. The cloth was formed by a number of variants of netting, twining and twilling on a false loom. It is a curious fact that in spite of some presumptive contact with Mexico, there was no cotton in the Southeast either in prehistoric or early historic times although there was in the Southwest. The cloth was also used for head bands, loin cloths, mantles and bags.

In the fired remains of the basins and with cremations there were fragments of engraved wooden bowls and other objects almost totally consumed by the conflagration. We should assume a considerable art expression in wood both in moveable objects and in house, council and mortuary structures.

The Hopewell people obtained pearls in startling numbers. They were for single or multiple strand necklaces, but were also placed around the wrists and ankles and perhaps used for bead embroidery. They were used as insets for eyes in the sculptured pipes and implanted in some of the copper headdresses and in carved bear canines used as toggles for clothing. Close to 40,000 pearls were recovered from the Turner site and probably more than that from the Hopewell site. While these may be fresh water pearls, that fact has not been settled nor do we know the source or sources for them.

One of the more striking exotic materials is the black obsidian or volcanic glass that was first recognized from Hopewell mounds in the middle of the last century. Subsequent study has gradually produced more information about it. We know that obsidian is almost entirely limited in the midwest to Hopewellian sites from Ohio to Illinois and southwestern Wisconsin. Within that cultural group 90 to 95 percent has come from the Hopewell site. At Hopewell the obsidian was manufactured into a series of superb large ceremonial spears or knives in a variety of forms. They range in form but most of them were shapes which are known in other lithic specimens. They range in size from three or four to over fifteen inches in length. In one great fired cache from the Hopewell site it is estimated there were over five hundred of these remarkable specimens. In another mound a single partly cremated burial had with him over three hundred pounds of worked obsidian fragments. The implements of obsidian here should probably be regarded as symbolic and as art forms. In the western Hopewellian sites however, there has been very little in any one site, normally the artifacts are utilitarian. The only significant number of large spears or knives outside of Ohio is in southwestern Wisconsin. During the last decade neutron activation studies of the trace minerals in the obsidian from a large number of Hopewellian sites demonstrated that the obsidian was obtained from a number of distinct flows in the Yellowstone National Park area, including that majestic exposure known as Obsidian Cliff.

Another far western source for specialized artistic productions of forms resembling normal implements is the Knife River locality in North Dakota. This is a southern tributary of the Missouri and from this region the Hopewell Indians obtained a distinctive brownish translucent mottled chalcedony known as Knife River flint. At many of the sites in Ohio, Illinois, Iowa and Wisconsin where obsidian is known we also find specimens of this material.

The same type of burial or ceremonial caches of raw materials that we have mentioned for earlier periods was carried to extremes. At one small mound at the Hopewell site over 8,200 flint discs or preforms were found in one mass. Similar large aggregates are known from a series of mounds in the Illinois Valley where well over 20,000 have been counted (782-793). These could well have provided raw material for the production of more finished items (810). Many of the projectiles and knives in the Cincinnati Art Museum collection are made from the same nodular blue gray flint that was used by earlier people, or from the Flint Ridge quarries which were the preferred source for the populations in the Scioto Valley. The shapes have changed from the Early Woodland period and there are remarkably similar forms at the many sites of this period in the Middle West.

Many of the ground and polished stone forms both ornamental and utilitarian continued in use. These include gorgets and pendants of a number of forms (765, 768-771), the axe and the celt (781, 776-780). Marine shells were imported from the large *Busycon, Cassis* and *Fasciolaria* which were hollowed out and used as large containers to smaller shells such as *Marginella, Oliva, Olivella,* and others which were formed into beads, added to necklaces or attached to clothing. The attraction to marine forms was not limited to molluscs for barracuda jaws, ornaments carved from marine tortoise shell and shark teeth were also obtained. Alligator teeth were obtained from the southeast and also used as parts of necklaces.

The Hopewell economy was still primarily hunting, fishing, fowling, and gathering. When nature was bountiful their diet was well balanced. They must still have had segments of their social groups dispersed at different seasons for food acquisition and for the several foreign materials small parties may well have made extensive trips to obtain them from Yellowstone, the sea coast and North Carolina. There was some amount of corn growing but the amount recovered is not large and does not indicate it was yet a significant source of food. The corn almost certainly comes into the Middle West across the Plains from the Southwest.

The houses that have been found are usually square to rectangular. The width varies a bit from 34 to 40 feet while the length may be from slightly more than 35 to over 50 feet. Some of the houses in Illinois are ovoid. These are multiple family units and have so far been identified in Ohio under mounds or within earthworks. There are also some smaller structures. Because of the lack of good information on the probable number of houses and the length of occupation of any of the sites in very precise terms we cannot give a good indication of the size of the social unit that occupied the large earthwork groups or even the smaller sites. Populations of from several hundred to perhaps five hundred may have been participating together at the major sites while much smaller numbers would be normal at most of the Middle Woodland Hopewellian sites. Population density would still not be much more than 1 per square mile. Minor variations can also be noticed in cultural patterns in the several river valleys such as the Muskingum, Scioto and Miami in Ohio, in the several sections of the Illinois Valley and so on. These reflect societal groupings or "tribes" each of them probably with several subdivisions.

The Illinois area has a large number of sites of this period and shares many artifact forms and behavior patterns with the southern Ohio populations, but the geometric earthworks are almost entirely missing and none of the burial procedures or the practices associated with acquiring burial furniture approach the Ohio area. However for reasons not too well understood Illinois Valley Hopewellian societies seem to have expanded much more than did the Ohio societies. The Middle Woodland Hopewell occupations in northern Indiana, western Michigan and the Saginaw Valley were derived from and maintained continuing contact with Illinois. Illinois Valley influences were also strong in Wisconsin, northeast Iowa, central and western Missouri around Kansas City and into northeastern Oklahoma. Finally, their burial practices and some materials penetrated down the Mississippi Valley as far as the Natchez area. To the north and east of these predominantly Hopewellian societies were other Middle Woodland groups who shared some of the changes in projectile point styles, ceramic techniques and shifts in burial practices. Burial mounds appear in some of these areas for the time but the ceremonialism associated with the disposal of the dead did not reach the heights it did in the midwest.

In the Lower Mississippi Valley and Southeast many sites have been sampled that belong to this period but there are no complete well rounded excavations. Here too the way of life has been developed and becomes clearly recognizable as constituting areal variants based primarily on clusterings of ceramic styles in the various environmental areas. One such area is in the alluvial flood plain of the Mississippi south of Memphis where a major group developed divisible into several smaller units. Another such major unit may be seen in central and southern Georgia where it is associated with a distinctive type of surface finish of pottery produced by pressing the still plastic exterior with wooden or clay stamp thus causing the so-called complicated stamped ware of the south Appalachians.

Late Woodland

For unknown reasons many of the cultural practices and materials that distinguished and identified the Middle Woodland Hopewellian cultures gradually disappeared or changed to new forms. In every area where regional enclaves can be recognized this change took place into societies which are called Late Woodland in much of the eastern part of the country. This change took place in the Midwest between A.D. 300 and 400. In central Ohio for many years certain burial practices and artifacts were found intrusive into the previously constructed Hopewell mounds. Around Cincinnati the complex has been named after an Indian occupation near the small town of Newtown. In some areas of the east and Great Lakes the older Woodland pattern of life was maintained with modifications up to the historic period and so the term Late Woodland applied to such entities is more of a cultural than a temporal term after about A.D. 1000-1400.

In the Mississippi Valley particularly between A.D. 700-1000 there were cultural changes which mark the beginning of the Mississippi Period which while continuing many of the earlier Indian patterns emphasized agriculture and other changes which made that great culture type a striking change from anything that had occurred earlier. Late Woodland is, in a way, a transitional period that includes a number of new developments which reach their culmination later. Late Woodland has some analogues to the European Dark Ages and is also temporally equivalent. Perhaps the stars?

In the Ohio area the pipe form changed from a platform with a short protruding section (825) to an elbow form (827). There were still a few effigy forms but they disappeared except for very rare examples. The elbow form took on many modifications and spread from the east into the southwest. Some of the modified platform style were introduced into northern Mexico from the Arkansas-Oklahoma area and began the use of pipe smoking there. Pipe smoking was still a custom which was restricted to relatively few and to special occasions. The celt (832-834) was by far the dominant heavy wood working tool. There are some number of gorget forms but they seem to disappear after about A.D. 400 to 1000.

Chipped and polished flint celts may well have had some use in working the soil either in digging pits or perhaps in early agricultural fields. A new form to appear was the ground and occasionally polished stone discoidal (830-831). These were used in games and become both larger and better made (876-881) in the next major period. One of the common projectile point forms of the early part of the period is illustrated (842) and is called the Lowe Flared Base after a location in the lower Wabash Valley, but after A.D. 700 the small triangular arrowpoint (847-854) made its appearance in a variety of forms and became the dominant form not only in the eastern United States but all over the country. The narrow thin flint blades struck from carefully prepared cores were no longer made.

The pottery takes on a very boring sameness in terms of the plain or cord marked surfaces. Most of the vessels are simple wide mouth jars with sub-conoidal bases. During the early part of the period there is very little decoration but with time the outer rim area becomes modified with single cord impressed designs, or cord wrapped around a dowel which is then impressed into the clay before firing, or other variants of these rather simple concepts. Shoulders become noticeable on some vessels and some acquire a collared appearance through a thickening of the upper rim. Local patterns can be recognized but the general trend is followed from the Atlantic well into the eastern Plains.

Most of the Late Woodland houses were smaller with many of them clearly being circular single family dwellings although some larger structures of 24 to 36 feet in diameter may well have housed a larger closely related social group. Very few of the village sites of the early part of this period have been adequately excavated but by A.D. 700-900 in the upper Ohio Valley villages were arranged in a circular pattern with an open central courtyard and log palisade around the village. A number of things may help account for some of these changes. The introduction of the bow and arrow is probably one factor. It is believed that this weapon, much more advanced than the atlatl, came into the east from the Plains. It was known in the extreme northwestern Plains in the first centuries A.D. and then reached the Southwest and the upper Mississippi Valley area about A.D. 700. It also appears likely that increased attention was being given to the planting of corn and squash. The resultant need for a more sedentary existence to take care of the crops and to protect themselves from the raids of neighbors resulted in the early rather simple stockades around villages.

The elaborate earthworks, the acquisition of exotic burial furniture and the considerable expenditure of energy and destruction by burial and burning of luxury goods and raw material came to a halt, mound burial still continued, adult males still receive most of the grave goods but there was a marked shift in customs and attitudes. This remarkable change in attitudes and behavior is not yet adequately understood. Only in the far southeast of adjacent Georgia, Florida and Alabama do some of these attitudes still seem to have continued but, of course, with the production of markedly different styles of pottery and other artifacts. The rich art expression in a variety of media and its symbolism and styles disappeared. Whether there was a shift to wood or leather we do not know.

While there may have been some minor population movements during the period none of any magnitude can be recognized. The populations in the Ohio and Illinois Valleys during the Middle Woodland period continued with gradual moderate change into and through the Late Woodland period. There does seem to be an increasing tendency for the head form to be somewhat broader in much of the southeast but this is not accentuated as much as it is in the next period.

The Mississippi Period and Cultures

During this period the area or areas of apparent dominance shift to the large flood plain of the Mississippi-Missouri around St. Louis and to the alluvial soils of the Mississippi Valley and the southeast. From St. Louis to Vicksburg a series of changes took place in ceramic forms, mound construction and other features which produced the Mississippian cultures. Their superiority was based upon corn agriculture which gave them a storable food supply to augment and to some degree supplant elements of their earlier diet. Their major villages through time became small towns. Their populations increased considerably. The size of the coherent organized social and political unit increased remarkably and by the time of the De Soto tour in the southeast A.D. 1536-1540 some groups claimed political control of and levied tribute from some of their neighbors. They were on their way to civilization!

It had taken a long time for the prehistoric Indians to learn the location of many of the minerals and plants they incorporated into their technology. It also must have taken some period of time to identify the soil types best suited to their agricultural skills but learn they did and also the northern and western limits of successful crop development. The house form changed to rectangular and many of the houses were single family or extended family dwellings. By A.D. 1000-1200 some of the larger villages were carefully planned and laid out in rows with minor groupings within the village probably conforming to social segments of the community and some houses to specialized functions or crafts. The dominant feature of Mississippi towns was an open court yard area associated with platform mounds of earth which were substructures for council houses, charnel houses, "chief's" houses and other societal functions. The mound-plaza concept as a central place for the most important civil and religious activities was also the center for the periodic dances and ceremonies during the year. The earliest sites in the Lower Mississippi Valley had one or two small mounds of this type but as time passed the village size increased and the mound size through successive rebuildings of the wood structures grew to considerable size.

The large Mississippian sites are as far north as southern Wisconsin, south to south-central Louisiana, west into northeast Texas and eastern Oklahoma and east as far as the southern Piedmont and northern Florida. In the Ohio Valley the last major prehistoric culture became a somewhat diluted Mississippian expression. One of the more famous sites is Aztalan, a fortified town about halfway between Madison and Milwaukee, Wisconsin. It includes some 20 acres within its palisaded and bastioned walls. The great site at Cahokia in the American Bottoms opposite St. Louis has a state park enclosing a small portion of the area between Alton and Columbia, Illinois, that was occupied by Indian groups in some ten villages or towns

912

and more than fifty smaller farming communities. This mammoth Monks Mound is over 1000 feet long, over 700 feet wide and over 100 feet high. It covers more ground than the great majority of Middle Woodland sites. The palisaded stockade that screened and protected a central area enclosing Monks Mound and fifteen others, took in some 200 acres. The central occupied area of Cahokia took in from 200 to 300 acres. The difficulty in estimating population size is that there is scant data on the number of dwelling units occupied contemporaneously, on the number and size of houses, or on determinations based on the skeletal population for very few burials have been found. For these reasons estimates have varied from 5000 to 50,000 for Cahokia during its major period from A.D. 1000-1300.

The Linn site in southwestern Illinois was a palisaded town of 30 acres. The Kincaid site in southeastern Illinois partially excavated by the University of Chicago covers some 125 acres. The Angel site in southwestern Indiana, just east of Evansville, has been partially excavated by the Indiana Historical Society. It now has a small museum building and is a State Memorial. Moundville in Alabama just south of Tuscaloosa contained some 34 mounds some of them of large size and covers some 175 acres. It is now a State Park. Etowah, near Cartersville, Georgia, had 3 large major mounds and a large village area of some 40 acres enclosed within a large ditch or moat connected to the Etowah River. There were hundreds of such sites in the mid-south within the area mentioned above. Some of them were seen and recorded by early Spanish, French and English who were able to observe the Indians in their normal activities during the sixteenth and seventeenth centuries.

The resemblance of the pyramid and plaza concept, to prehistoric and early historic Mexican life is quite apparent. In addition there are a few design concepts and other features from a number of different sites in the Southeast that suggest Mexican origin. There are however a number of difficulties to the interpretation of Mexican-Southeastern relationships. No Mexican made artifacts are known to have been found in any kind of controlled conditions, let alone any sites with a significant amount of such material. The items of resemblance are often from widely scattered localities and are expressed in what are clearly local art styles. Some of the design concepts such as the step triangle and cloud symbol are also known in the Southwest. The various features suggestive of prehistoric Mexico appear in the southeast and Mississippi Valley but not within either a short time period or a restricted area. On the other hand there are enough suggestions of some specific ideas from Mexico, such as that of the heart engraved on Moundville vessels or the skull and cross bones also at Moundville, that some sort of contact seems indicated. It is more likely that a few Mexican merchant traders may have succeeded in crossing the forbidding northern Tamaulipas and southeast Texas area into the southeast and brought with them some features of Mexican culture which could be incorporated into the Southeastern religious symbolism. Statements of connections, importations or influences from Mexico which go much beyond this must be regarded as unwarranted.

The Mississippi economy was changed by the striking development of maize agriculture and finally the introduction of the bean sometime between A.D. 1000-1200. This final major addition to their cultivated crops appears to have entered the east from the Southwest which in turn had received the bean from Mexico. Corn was stored both in above ground granaries and in sub-surface carefully prepared pits. In the central part of the Mississippi Valley flint hoes of a number of styles (871-875) came into use. In many areas however a wooden digging stick or sometimes heavy shells (969), large animal shoulder blade or elk antler (1015) was used for hoeing. In the deep south staggered planting allowed them to have fields maturing over a period of months in the late summer and fall. The forested areas would have to be cleared and after some years of cropping would have to lie fallow. Fields in many of the alluvial valleys while subject to damage through flooding did however have their fertility improved by such acts of nature. In addition to the cultivated food the varieties of oak, hickory, walnut and pecan added their bounty in the fall, and fruit would add to their diet from early spring into the fall. Migratory waterfowl and local birds, river and lake fish added protein, but the main source of protein was from animals of which the deer was by far the most common furnishing from 90 to 95 percent of the dressed meat.

One of the most immediately striking changes in the material culture is the pronounced change in the ceramic pattern. The pottery has a considerable variety of forms fulfilling different functions and is coil built, modelled, incised, engraved and painted in a number of different styles. Much of the Mississippian pottery gradually becomes tempered with mussel shell fragments which was technically superior to other earlier temper. A rather wide mouth plain surface jar becomes the normal cooking and storage form. Handles on jars in the early phases are rounded or rope shape and in the later are strap shaped. The more common utilitarian ware of northeastern Arkansas has relatively coarse shell temper and is called Neeley's Ferry Plain (893-900) but a much finer temper, paste and surface finish was made for bowl and fine effigy forms which is referred to as Bell Plain (884-892). Some of the decorated forms on Neeley's Ferry paste are named after specific sites such as Rhodes Incised (903-904), Walls Engraved (907), and in painted types Old Town Red (909, 910), Carson Red-on-Buff, and Avenue Polychrome (912-916). The Cincinnati Art Museum collection of this northeast Arkansas pottery contains some outstanding examples of their craftsmanship. Other areas of the southeast also have distinctive regional styles and shapes which almost certainly conform to late prehistoric cultural groups of closely related populations.

The predominant hunting and war implement was the bow and arrow. The arrow shaft had points made of flint in plain triangular or side-notched forms (882), or had bone or antler points. Spear or knife blades were large triangular or large leaf-shaped forms. Some of these latter were placed with burials of priests and may well have been employed in ceremonies associated with warfare or sacrificial victims. The latter is suggested by engraved representations of such activities on marine shell gorgets. Carefully made and finished discoidal stones were employed in the chunky game which was played by many southeastern groups (876-881).

The elbow pipe of stone or baked clay was given a considerable number of different shapes (917). In addition there were clay and stone effigy forms ranging from a few inches high to rather massive stone forms. Some of these animal and human forms are superb examples of the sculptor's art. Those of a reddish bauxite from the Arkansas valley near the Oklahoma-Arkansas border are particularly outstanding. Pairs of sculptured stone human figures have been recovered from a number of major Mississippian sites in Tennessee and in north Georgia. One pair, two feet high from Etowah were of marble. They had sculptured representations of head and hair dress, skirt and belt and the figures were painted with red on the ears, white eyes with black pupils, and a painted elaborate chest piece for the male. These may well have represented specific deceased individuals enclosed within that particular tomb.

With important burials there are strings of shell beads ranging up into the hundreds made from small local or marine forms or cut and ground from larger fresh or salt water species. At Cahokia a number of caches of moderate size marine shells in the several hundreds, and hundreds of sections of unfinished beads, and of finished beads along with the perforators, and sandstone saws and abraders to finish the manufacture, have been recorded. These identify the area as the locale of such manufacture from imported raw material to the complete form. There is no evidence that such manufactured goods were for anything other than local consumption.

Copper was still used to some degree for beads and for copper axes and adzes but its most striking function was for thin plates which were shaped into religious symbols and embossed with elaborate designs of priests in their active ceremonial dress wearing feather robes and complex headdresses. All of the several items portrayed on these copper plates have been found with burials in the southeast. Scenes from ceremonial activities, or their religious symbolism were engraved on large marine shells or on circular gorgets of shell. These art forms were made at a number of major centers such as Spiro in eastern Oklahoma, and at a number of sites in eastern Tennessee. Both the regional styles and temporal variants within them can be recognized. From eastern Tennessee the scalloped edge (863), rattlesnake (861) and mask gorget (855-860) were traded to neighboring societies as well as having a prominent place in the burial ceremonies of the upper Tennessee drainage. Cylindrical shell hair pins are commonly associated with status burials (864-865). In major southeastern sites certain groups of burials were accorded more time and attention and considerably more and better made grave goods were placed with them. These are the burials of the societies' civil and religious leaders who were accorded in death a full measure of their position and of the necessary means to carry out this role in the hereafter.

The Mississippian culture represented in the southern Ohio, and adjacent area is known as the Fort Ancient culture. While the earthworks at Fort Ancient were constructed by Hopewell people, populations of Fort Ancient culture did live in the valley of the Little Miami in close proximity, and there was some habitational and burial activity in the southern part of the Fort. This cultural complex gradually developed primarily from Late Woodland populations, influenced by Mississippian developments to the west and south, and by the increased population and resultant societal needs from the growth of agriculture. The major river valleys are again an important factor in assisting social and other relationships between populations within their valleys.

The Fort Ancient culture has a very similar distribution in Ohio to that of the much earlier Hopewell culture, but Fort Ancient also extended into Kentucky particularly, and into West Virginia with much greater strength than did Hopewell. Along the Ohio River the sites by A.D. 1200-1400 were becoming very similar in many of their features to other Mississippi sites. One of the best known sites was located from Mariemont to Madisonville on the north side of the Little Miami River. Called Madisonville it, like many other sites, is now almost completely gone. Some of the materials from excavations in the last quarter of the last century are in the Cincinnati Art Museum collection and are an excellent representation of the crafts and arts of these late prehistoric Cincinnatians.

Fortunately the village soils were not acidic in nature so that both bone and shell tools and ornaments were unusually well preserved. Both elk and deer antler were shaped into forms such as hoes (1015), picks, arrowshaft straighteners (1018), spatulas, arrowpoints and flint chipping tools. Large mammal ribs carried transverse grooves and became musical rasps (1024, 1025), deer and elk leg bones were worked into shapes suitable for removing hair from hides and are called beamers (1027). There are a few harpoons not only for the large river fish but also for other game. Both mammal and bird bones were employed as awls in perforating, sewing, weaving and other common tasks (1000-1005). Deer jaws were used to scrape corn from the cob (1026). Bird bone was made into flutes (1023) and into fishhooks (1010-1011). Bird bones also were most suitable for the manufacture of beads (986), while the canine teeth of mammals became pendants or parts of necklaces (993-994).

Large thick walled mussel shells from the river were employed as hoes (969), while a different species was shaped into a spoon or scoop (970). The local fresh water molluscs provided material for a variety of bead forms, and these were augmented by strands made from marine shell. There were also pendants made of marine shell including some small whole *Busycon* shells. Very little copper was recovered from Madisonville but there are a few examples of European trade items such as glass beads, a brass bell (983) and some iron objects. The best estimate of the time period for the arrival of these European goods is in the last half of the seventeenth century before any European explorers had made their appearance in the Ohio Valley. The number of triangular arrowpoints and flint drills and scrapers from Madisonville must be well up in the thousands testifying not only to the size of the site but to its length of occupation which is estimated at between 400 to 500 years.

There were also a great many pipes of clay and stone. So many in fact that the suspicion is aroused that pipe smoking may have become more than a ceremonial activity. There were many different forms (926-933) from barrel shaped, jar shaped, disc shaped, effigy, elbow and other forms. Many unfinished pipes of limestone and sandstone were in the village. A large number of cannel coal ornaments shaped into effigy animal claws and teeth (978-982) or other forms for adornment were obtained. This is a common feature of many Fort Ancient sites along the Ohio river. Celts are the most common heavy woodworking tool.

By the time the Madisonville site was occupied all of the Fort Ancient pottery from there is shell tempered. There are a few bowls and salt pans (large shallow evaporating dishes for water from salt springs) but most of the vessels were cooking and storage jars with a very distinctive outward flare to the upper rim and with strap handles (924). A few vessels had a surface finish which resulted from patting the exterior with a grooved paddle (925) but most of the vessels have a plain or a cordmarked body. Some of the Madisonville vessels are quite unusual in the presence of a small animal effigy portrayed as climbing up the side of the vessel and about to lift its head above the lip (921). It is not clear what beast is intended but some of them resemble a salamander. A most unusual and probably unique vessel from Madisonville is the pedestal jar (920) that is part of the Cincinnati Art Museum Collection. While the pedestal is connected with bowls in the Near East, the Mediterranean, and ancient China and India it is not often associated with a jar. Why this combination turns up at Madisonville is one of those strange occurrences in human behavior that could hardly be predicted.

Summary

This brief presentation of some of the features of the gradual growth and development of Indian societies in the midcontinental area has had particular reference to some of the collections in the Cincinnati Art Museum which range over the whole span of prehistoric occupation. The long period of trial and error, invention and discovery that the native populations passed through is similar in many ways to the similar long periods of change which every human line has gone through in the thousands of years they have existed in the several regions of the world. The North American Indian achievements were remarkable. The great experiment of human cultural growth was interrupted and effectively destroyed. It is gone forever. Its works remain and a small portion are preserved. That heritage on this land is a vital part of human history.

James Bennett Griffin, Ph.D.
Professor of Anthropology and
Curator of Museum of Anthropology,
University of Michigan

Some Suggested Readings

Willey, Gorden R., *An Introduction to American Archaeology, Vol. 1, North and Middle America,* New York, Prentice-Hall, Inc., 1966.

Jennings, Jesse D., *Prehistory of North America,* New York, McGraw-Hill, 1968, revised 1974.

Griffin, James B., *Archeology of Eastern United States,* Chicago, University of Chicago Press, 1952.

Griffin, James B., *The Fort Ancient Aspect. Its Cultural and Chronological Position in Mississippi Valley Archaeology,* Ann Arbor, Museum of Anthropology Anthropological Paper No. 28, 1966 (Reprint of 1943 edition).

27

1

3

4

42

7

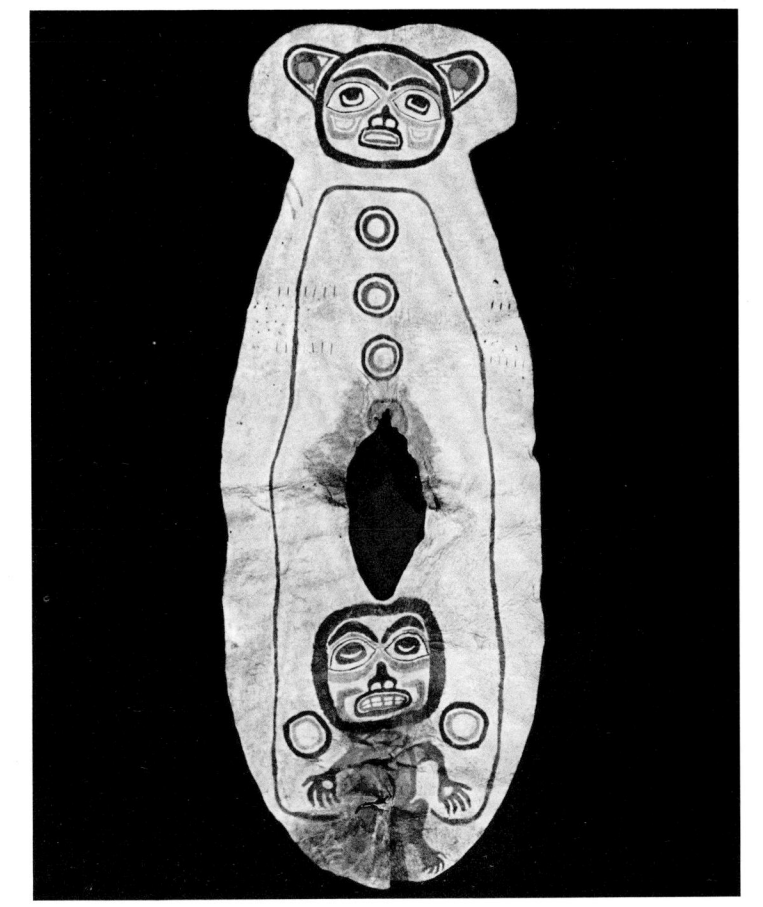

12

9

11

43

13

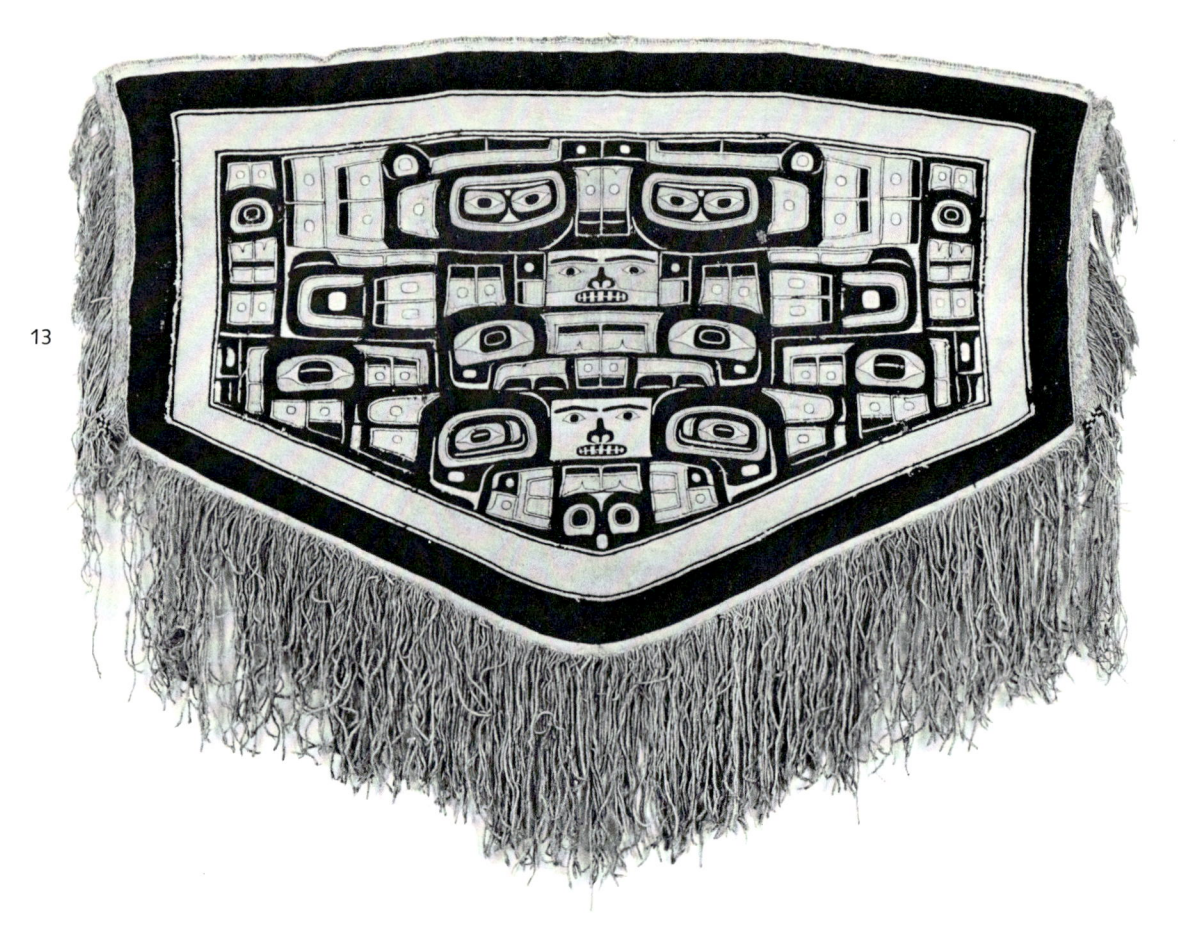

14

16

44

26

29

28

31

45

34, 35

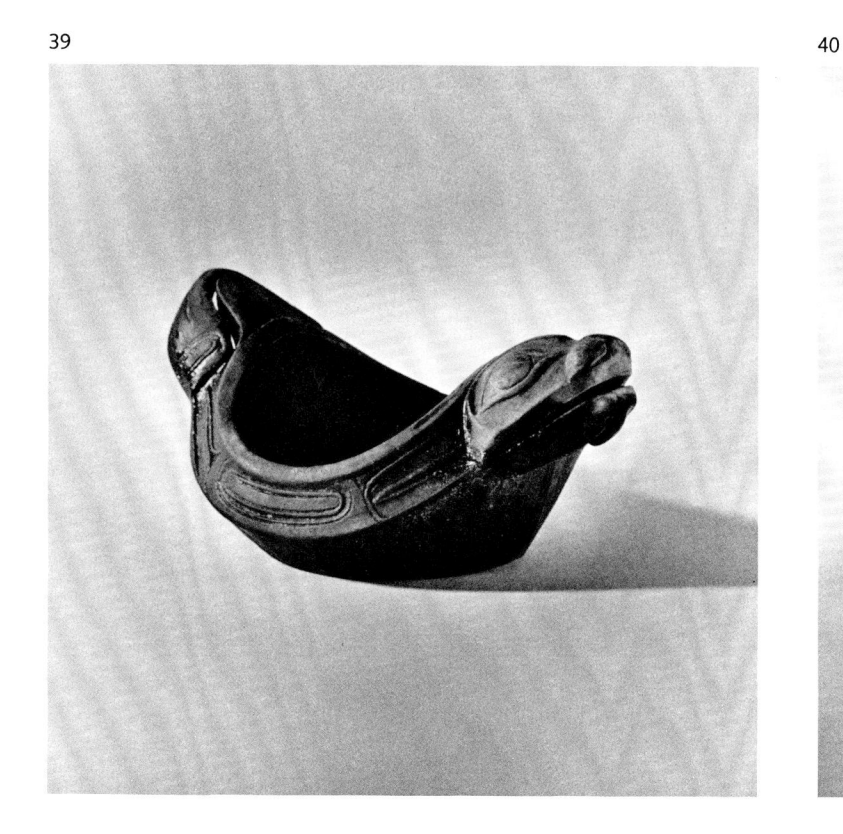

38

39

40

46

41

42

45

46

47

51

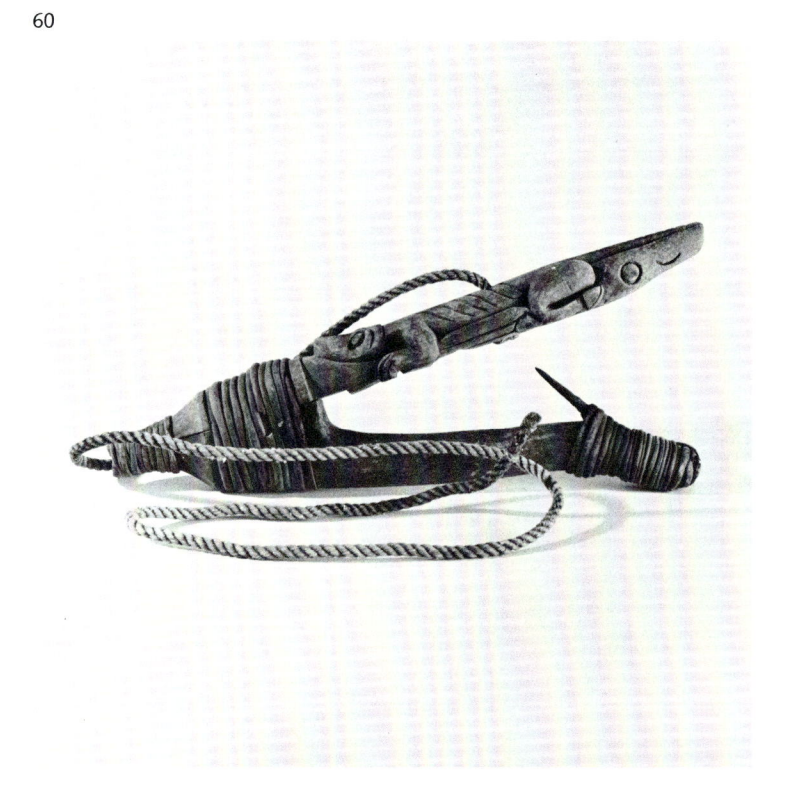

52

59

60

48

66

72

69

49

77

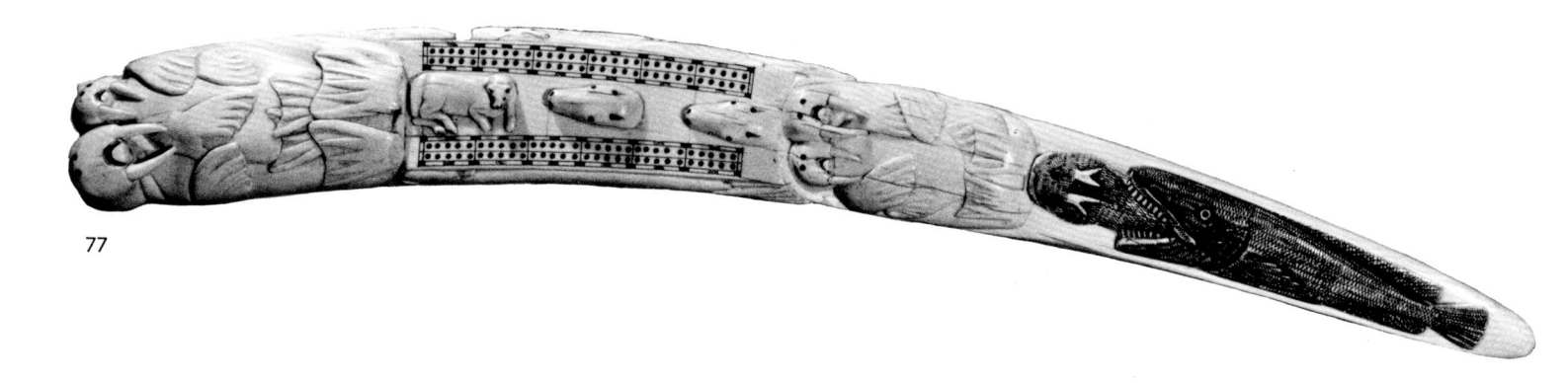

76

87

50

93

111

113, 114

149

133

51

162

167

52

175

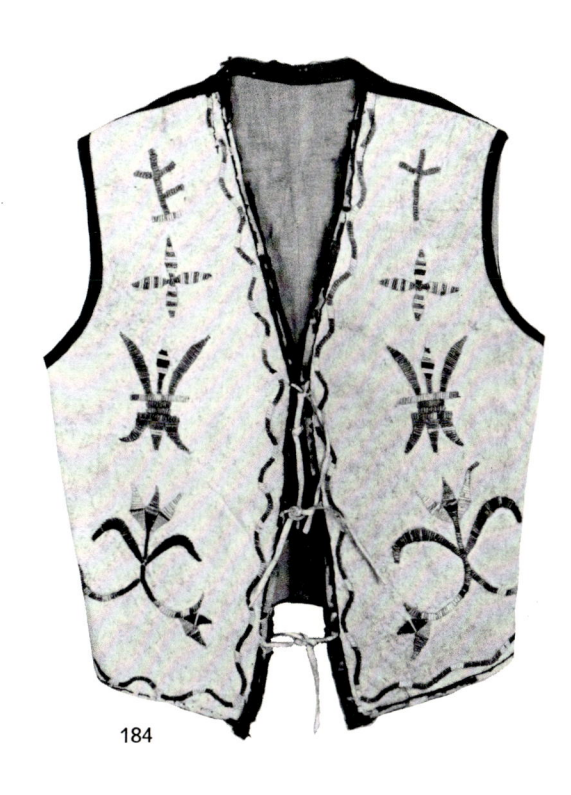

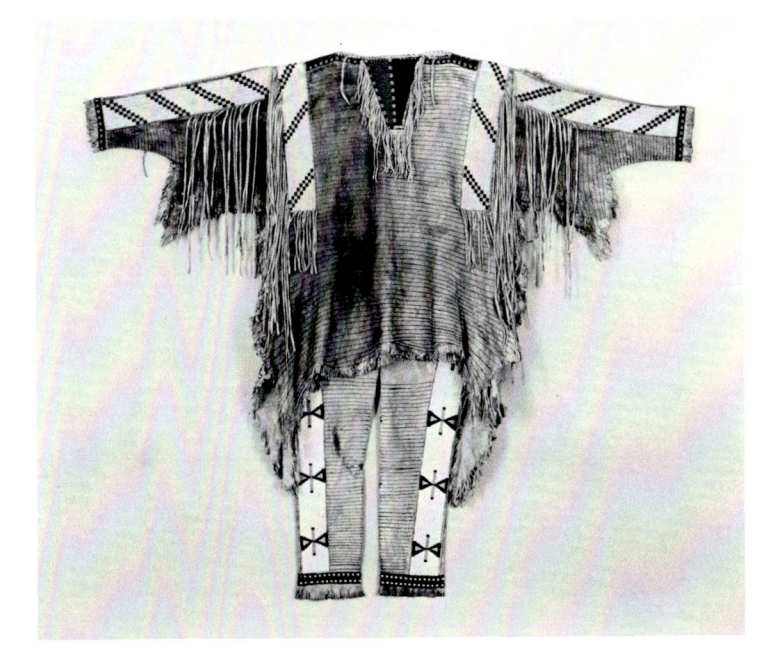

184

180, 181

194

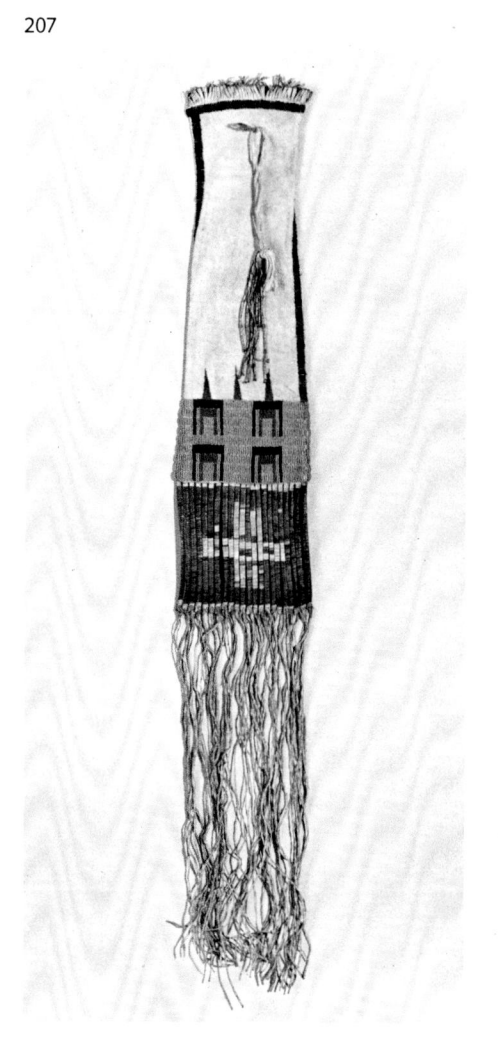

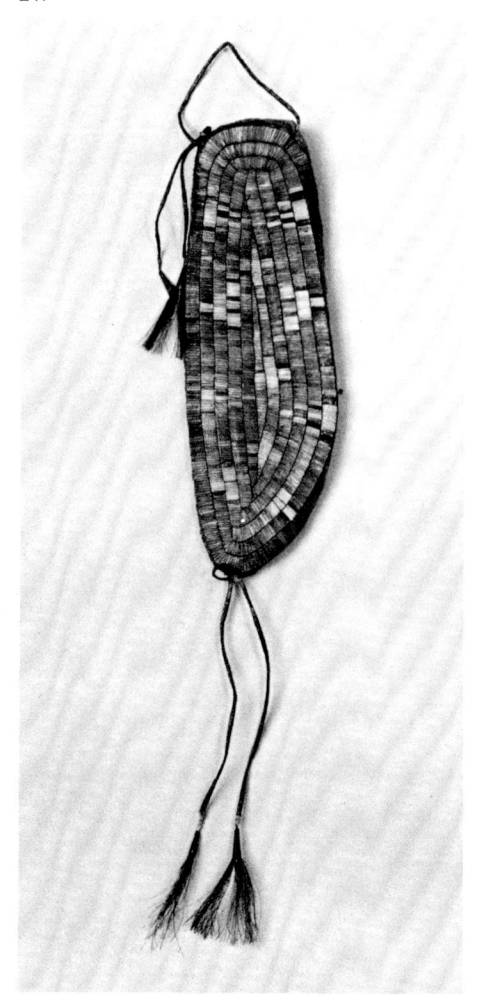

207

217

223

229

232

245

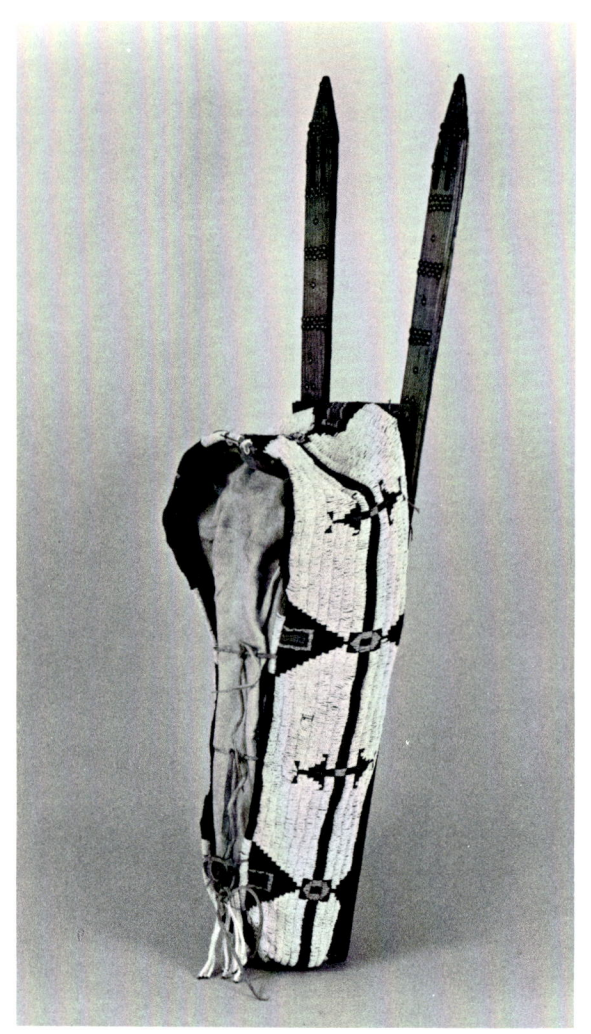

246

253

263

267

281

288

300

58

304

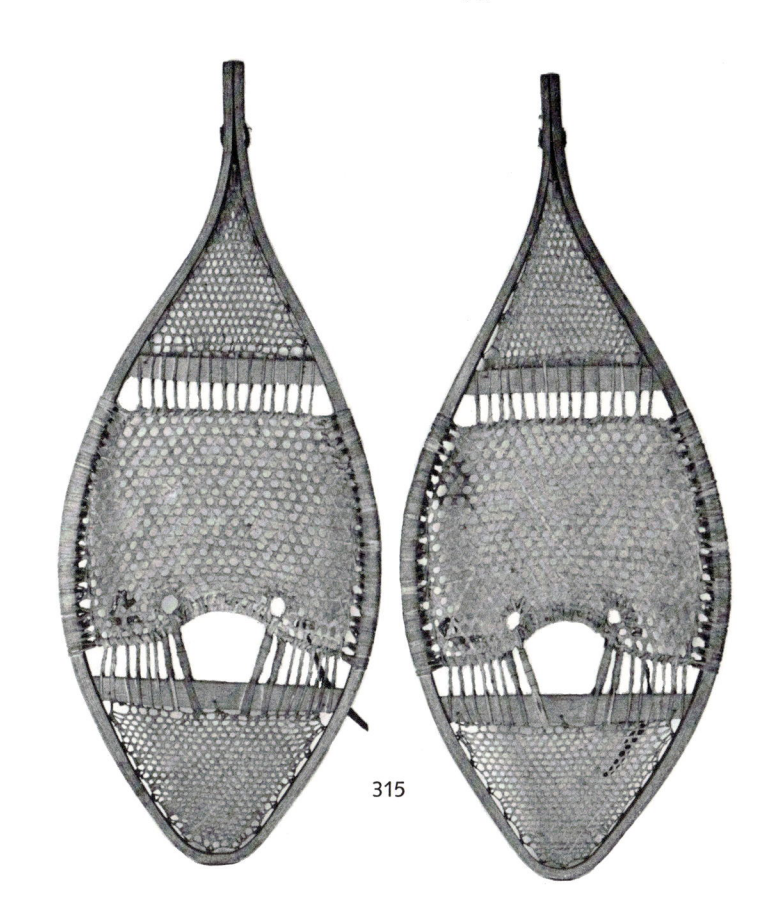

307

315

318

322

325

326

351

352

357

369

61

376

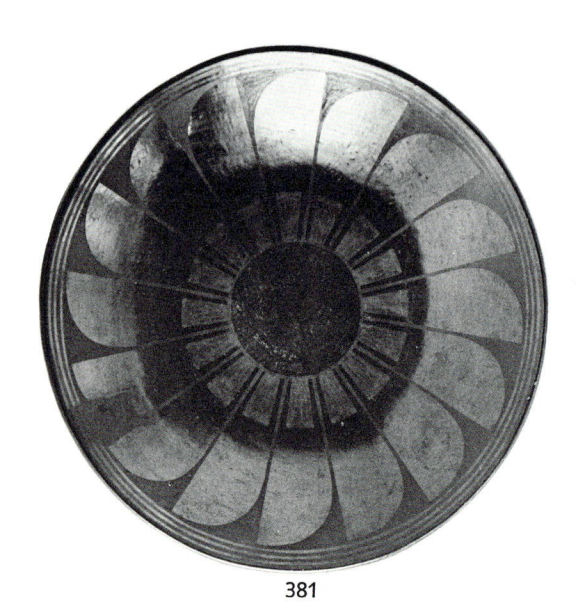

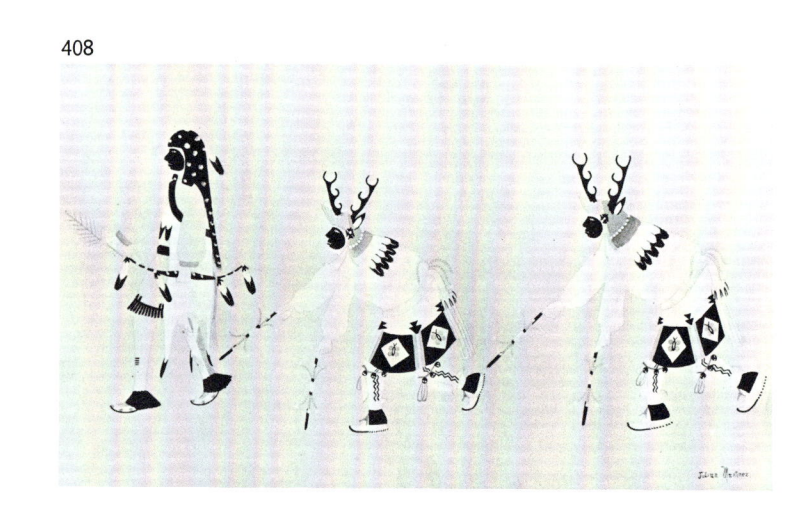

394

381

408

415

438

63

441

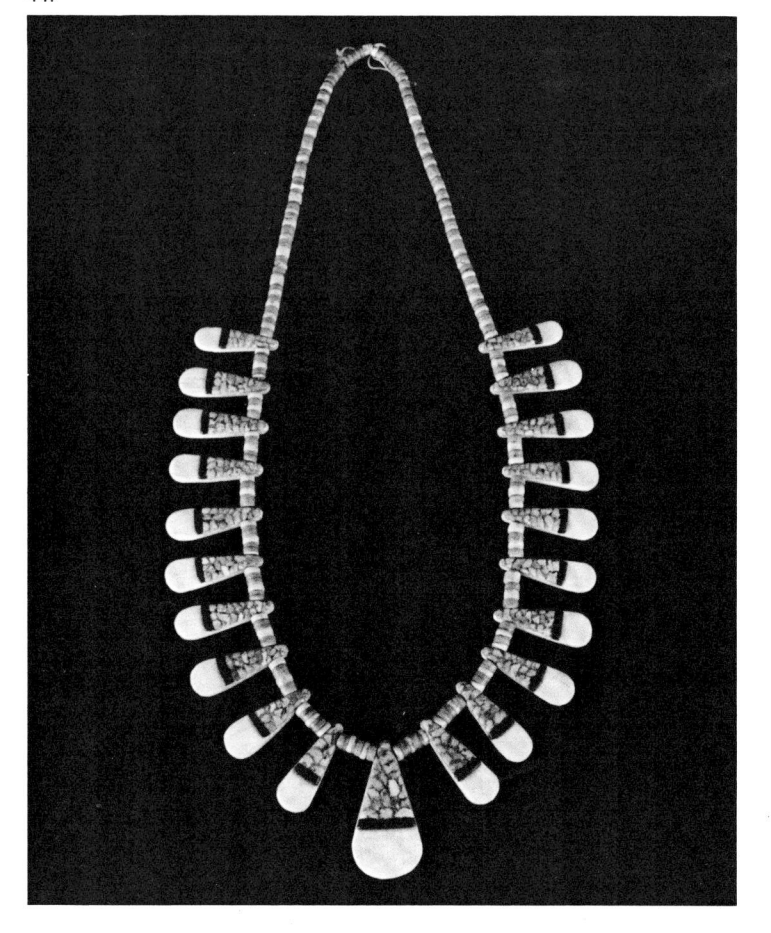

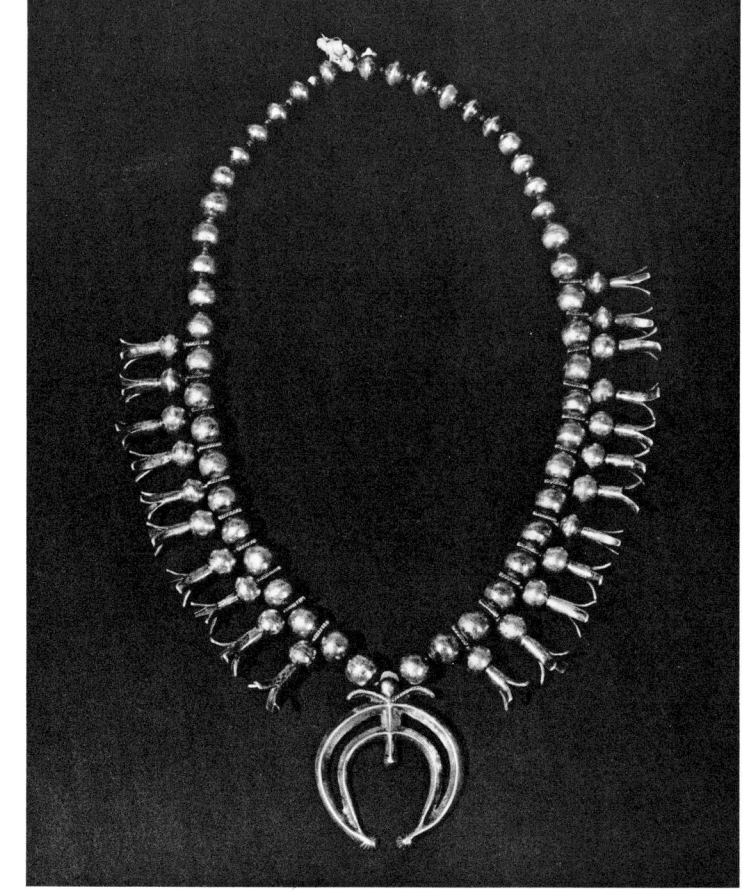

447

454

472

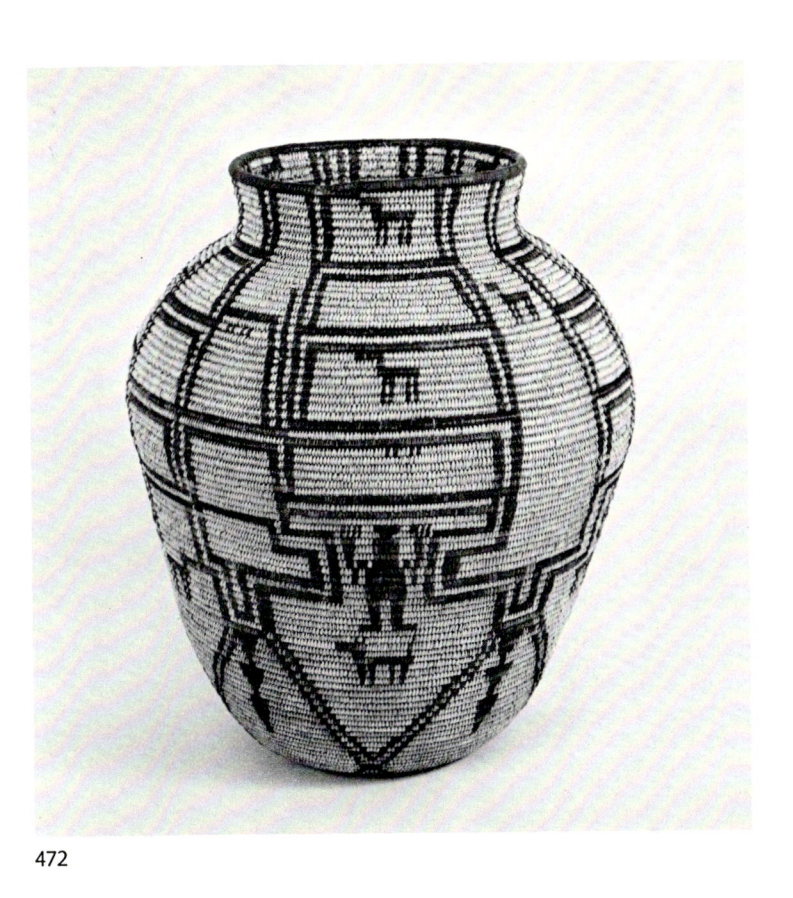

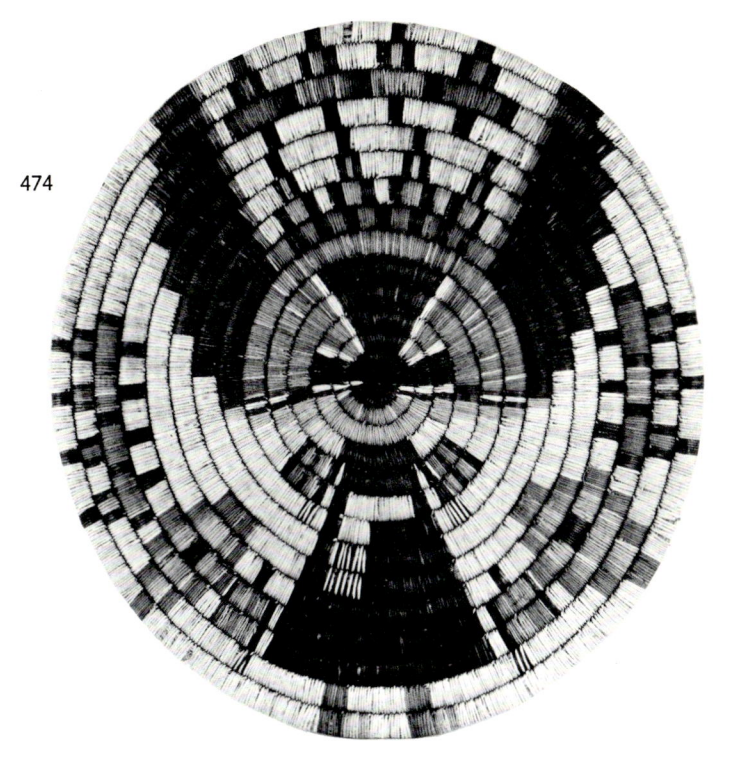

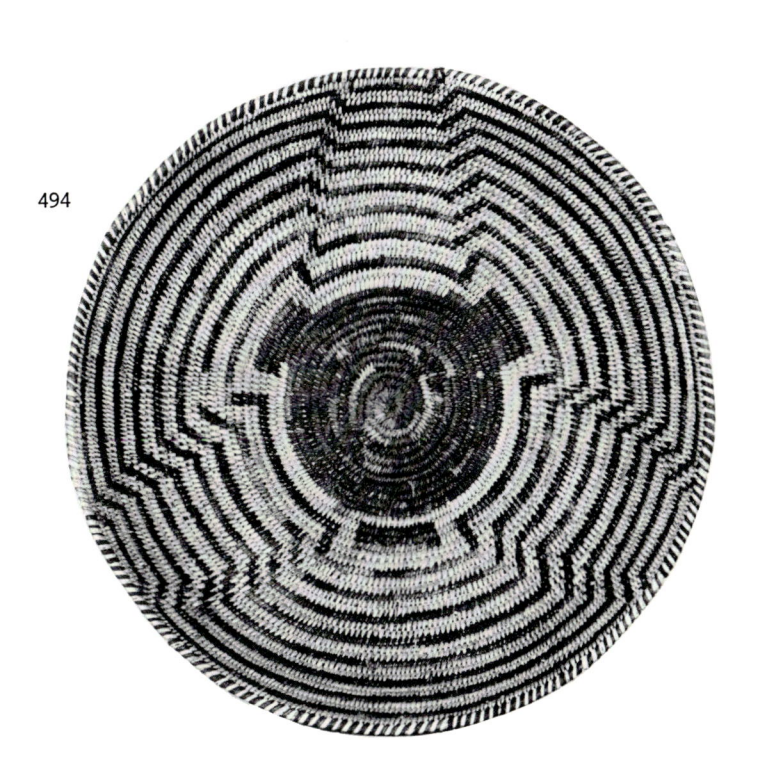

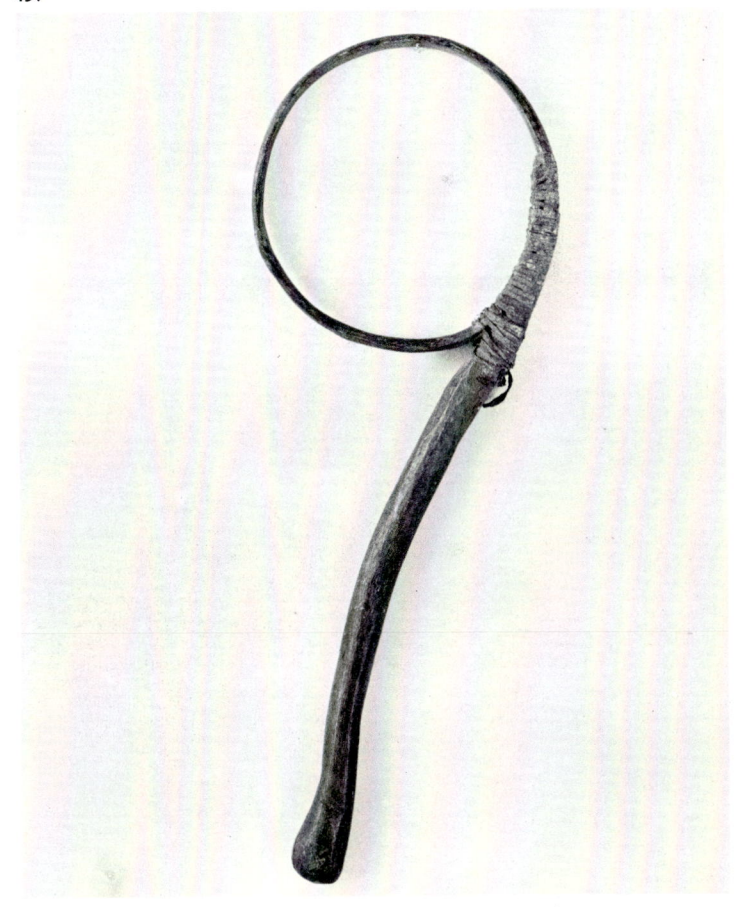

474

497

494

65

500

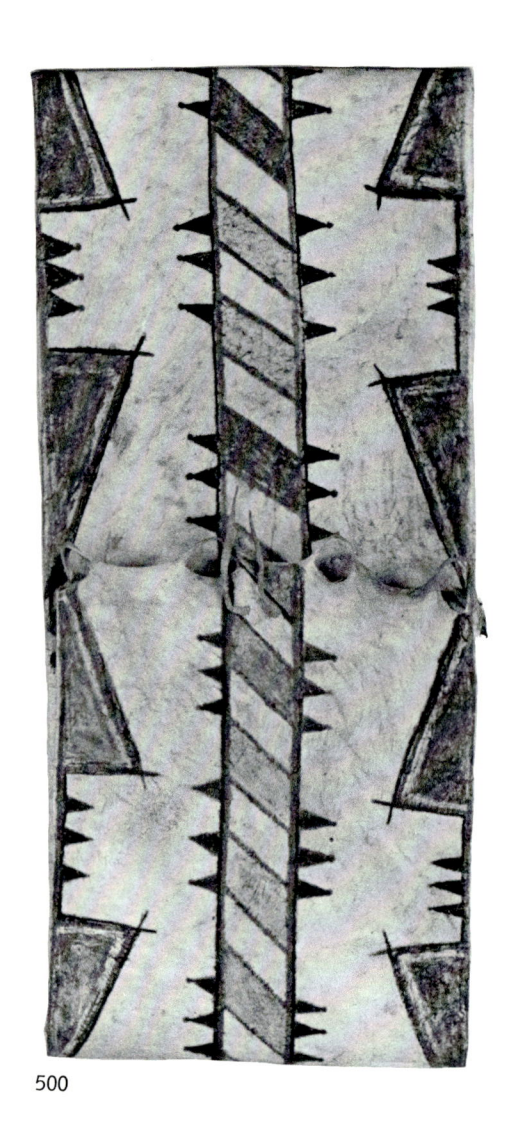

571, 573

609, 567

587, 619, 620

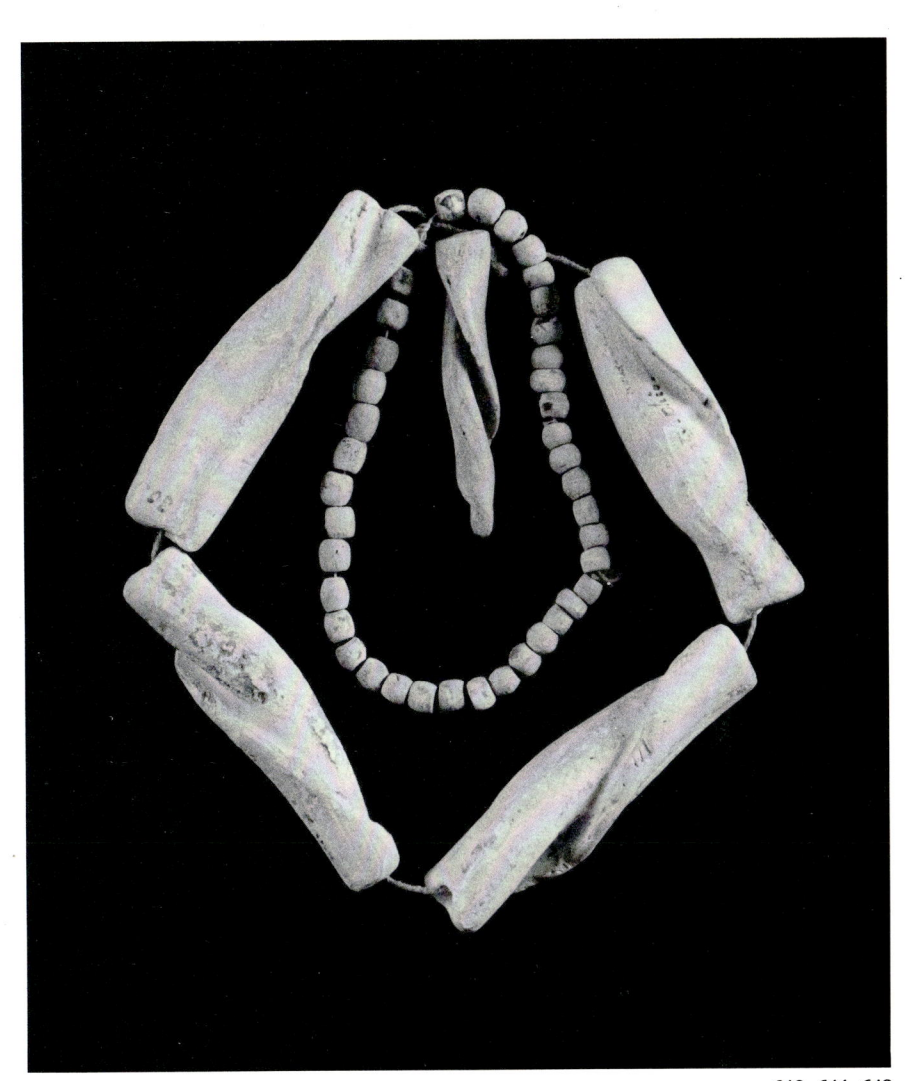

570, 594, 589

640, 641, 642

67

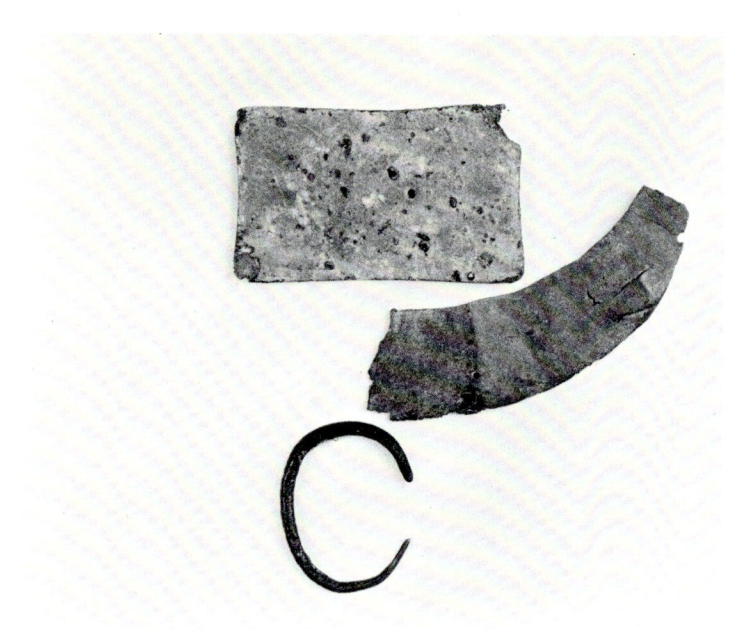

675, 676, 678

745, 752, 755, 694

760, 761, 762, 763

759, 781, 776

827, 775, 825

792, 797, 817, 814, 798, 811

771, 769

69

680, 681, 683

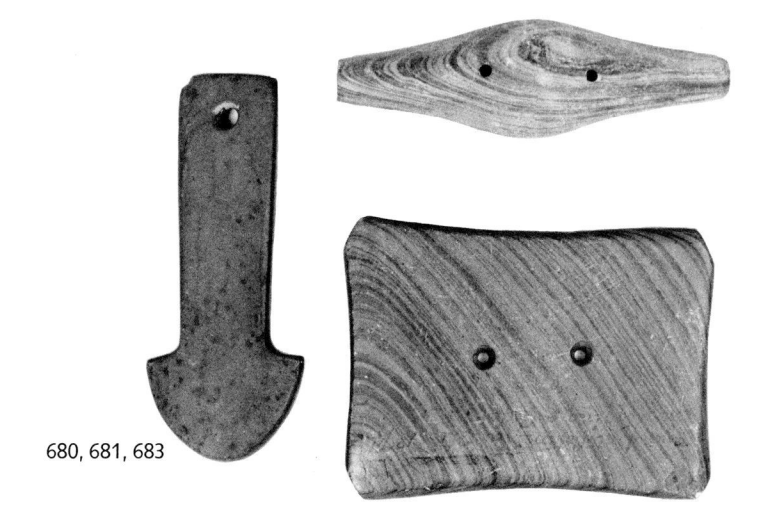

826

832, 833

879, 881

868, 871, 882

852, 853, 836, 842

71

900, 917

913, 916, 910

907, 905

892, 890

903, 904

921

901, 902

920

73

923, 924, 925

928, 933, 932, 926

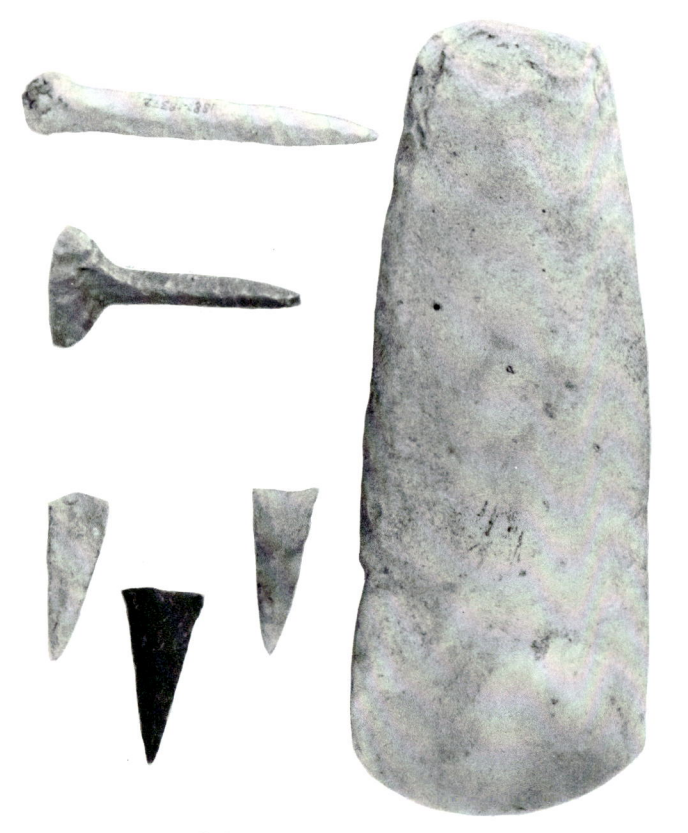

970, 969

972, 976, 948, 953, 954, 966

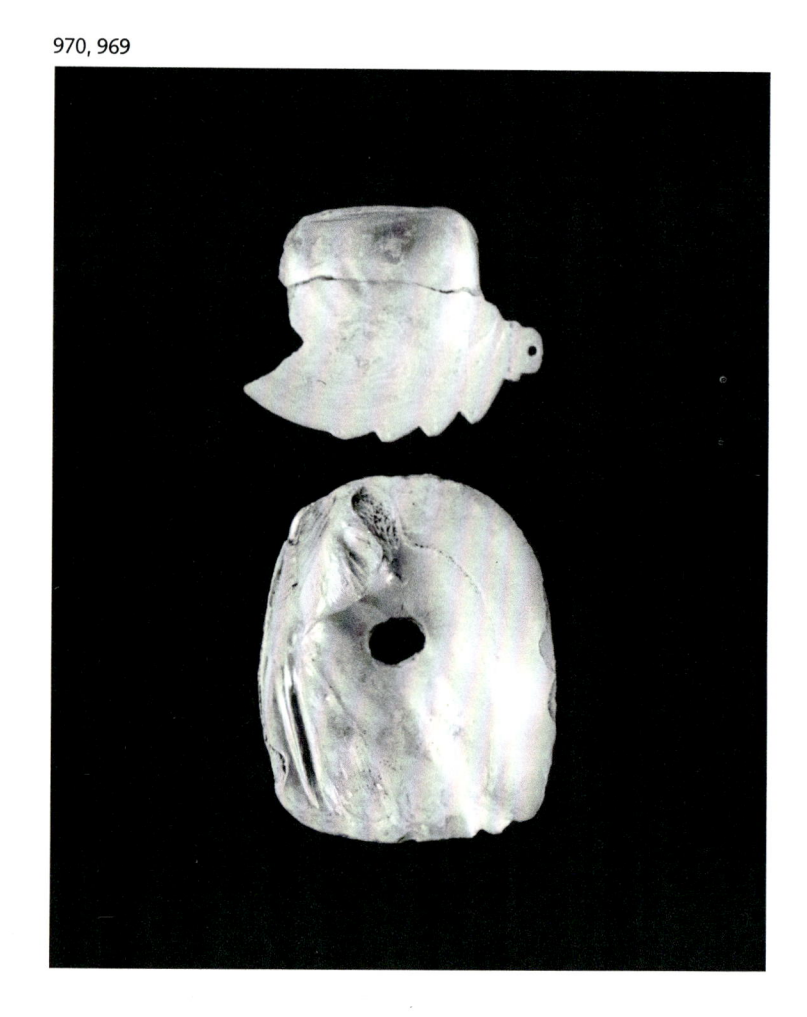

74

984, 981, 993, 994, 983, 978

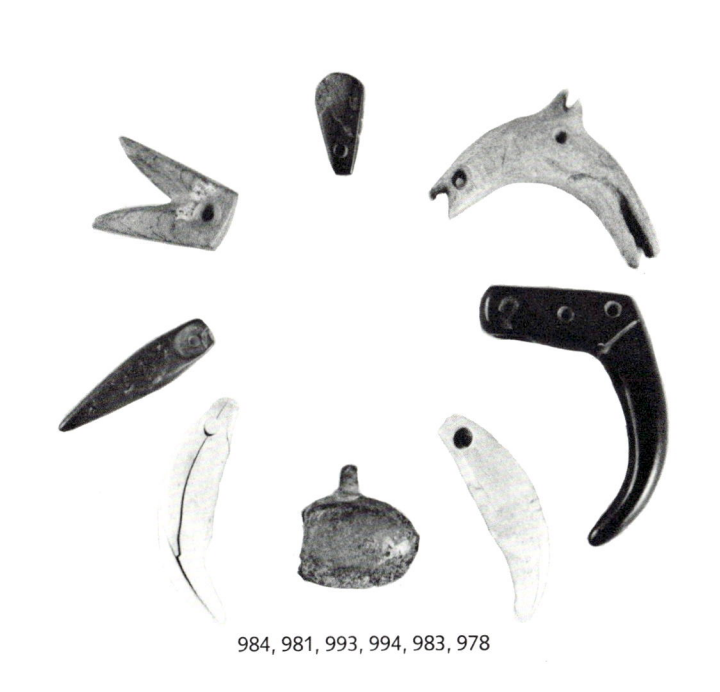

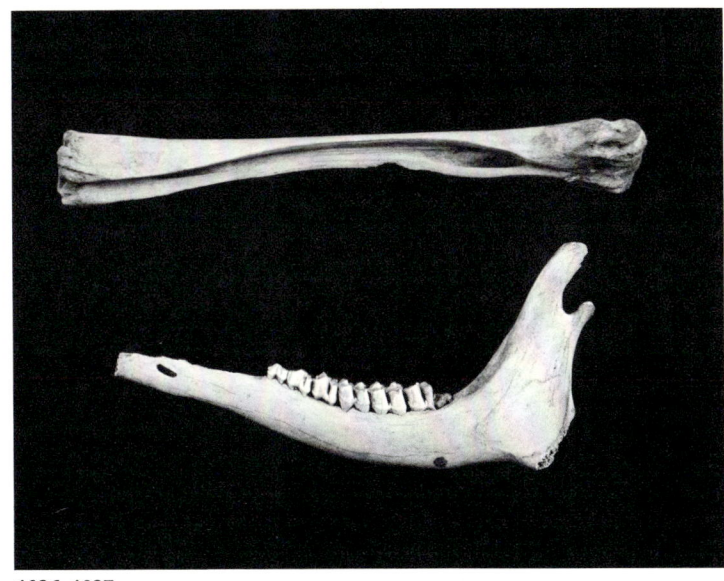

1026, 1027

1015, 1012, 1016

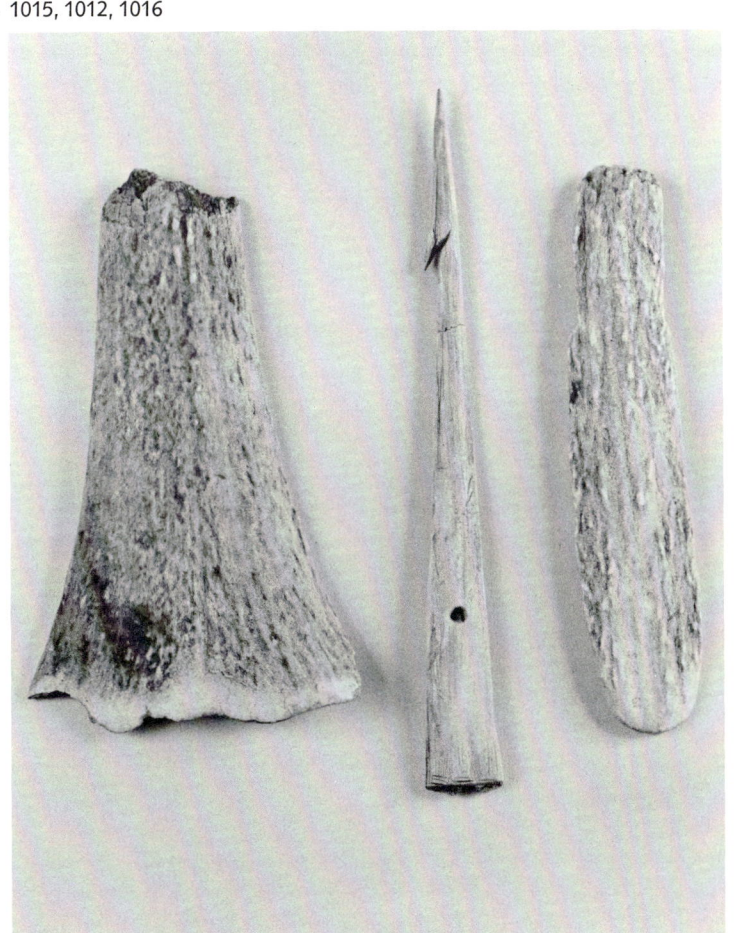

1010, 986, 1005, 1000, 1006

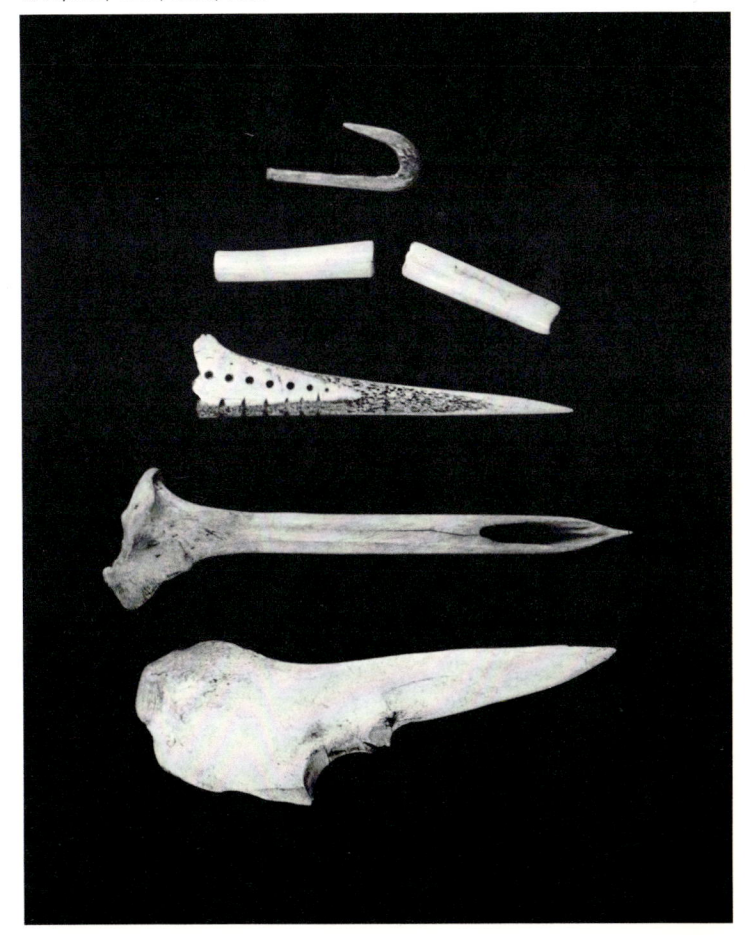

75

1024, 1023, 1018, 1020, 1007

Catalogue

*Items starred (*) are illustrated.
Dimensions are given in centimeters.*

The Northwest Coast

*1. **Tom-Tom,** painted hide on wood frame, diameter about 64.0, depth of frame about 7.7. Single head, painted on the under side with eagle or thunderbird in red and black. From Alaska, probably Tlingit or Haida tribe, XIX c. Gift of Dr. and Mrs. W. W. Seely, 1888.290.

2. **Tom-Tom,** painted hide on wood frame, diameter about 49.0, depth of frame 9.0. Single head with human (?) figure painted on under side in red and black. Tlingit tribe, Alaska, XIX c. Gift of William Howard Doane, 1914.70.

*3. **Raven Rattle,** carved and painted wood, length 32.0. Haida tribe, Alaska or Canada. XIX c. Gift of William Howard Doane, 1914.76.

*4. **Gobular Rattle,** carved and painted wood, length 26.7. Hawk-human mask carved and painted on obverse, painted bird-body elements on reverse, about five small clay (?) pellets inside, the two halves bound together with sinew on one side, a replacement on the other. Haida tribe, Queen Charlotte Island, Canada, XIX c. Gift of William Howard Doane, 1914.74.

5. **Gobular Rattle,** carved and painted wood, length 24.8. Hawk-human mask carved and painted on both sides with hand-forearms vertically beside mouth. Haida tribe, Queen Charlotte Island, Canada, XIX c. Gift of William Howard Doane, 1914.75.

6. **Pear-Shaped Rattle,** carved and painted wood, length 21.5. Head of eagle or thunderbird in relief on both sides, painted wing feathers depending from upper margin. Tlingit tribe, Alaska, XIX c. Gift of William Howard Doane, 1919.408.

*7. **Rattle in the Form of a Bird,** carved wood covered with multi-colored woven grasses, length 31.0. Recorded as obtained from Sekane tribe, British Columbia, XIX c., but style of work is more characteristic of Makah tribe of northern Washington and may have been traded to Sekane. Gift of William Howard Doane, 1919.409.

8. **Double-Circle Rattle,** wood, cloth and puffin beaks, diameter about 18.5. Tlingit tribe, Alaska, XIX c. Gift of William Howard Doane, 1914-71.

*9. **Whistle in the Form of a Human (?) Head,** carved wood, height 15.5. Faint vestiges of paint or stain. Probably once activated by an attached skin bladder bellows now missing. Haida tribe, British Columbia or Alaska. Bequest of Marguerite T. Doane, 1955.61.

*10. **Mantle,** black trade cloth with the mask of possibly a sea monster outlined in dentalium shells, fringe of puffin beaks, length from neck to knee about 80.0. From Alaska before 1888. Gift of Dr. and Mrs. W. W. Seely, 1888.284.

*11. **Mantle,** painted moose (?) hide, seal (?) shaped, length from shoulder to knee about 75. Chilkat tribe, Alaska, 1889, said to have belonged to Skundoo, a Chilkat shaman. Gift of Dr. and Mrs. W. W. Seely, 1889.297.

*12. **Mantle,** obverse painted cotton, reverse blue-black trade cloth and part of striped wool blanket, about 162.5 by 117.0. Chilkat tribe, Alaska, 1889, said to have belonged to Skundoo, a Chilkat shaman. Gift of Dr. and Mrs. W. W. Seely, 1889.296.

*13. **Blanket,** warp wool on cedar bark core, weft wool, about 172.5 by 103.0. Chilkat tribe, Alaska. Gift of Rebecca Scarborough and Mrs. Hugh Smythe, 1940.1038.

*14. **Necklace,** bone and ivory, knotted hide thongs, longest pendant about 26.0. Several pendants are decorated with incised circles, and one with incised mask and cross-hatched tail of beaver. Chilkat tribe, Alaska, 1889, said to have belonged to Skundoo, a Chilkat shaman. Gift of Dr. and Mrs. W. W. Seely, 1889.298.

15. **Rectangular Amulet, Circular Amulet,** incised slate strung on torn strip of cotton, diameter of disk about 3.9, rectangle 6.8 by 4.5. From Alaska before 1893. Gift of Lucien Wulsin, 1964.966.

*16. **Bracelet,** silver, width 3.3, diameter about 6.0. Engraved killer-whale motif. From Alaska before 1893. Gift of Lucien Wulsin, 1964.968.

17. **Bracelet,** silver, width .5, diameter about 6.5. One end represents the head of a snake, the other end the tail, with engraved decoration between. From Alaska before 1893. Gift of Lucien Wulsin, 1964.972.

18. **Bracelet,** silver, width .5, diameter about 6.2. Cut in relief pattern of lozenges with additional engravings. From Alaska before 1893. Gift of Lucien Wulsin, 1964.973.

19. **Bracelet,** silver, width .5, diameter about 6.9. Engraved foliate scrolls and crosshatching. From Alaska before 1893. Gift of Lucien Wulsin, 1964.974.

20. **Bracelet,** silver, width .3, diameter about 6.5. Engraved foliate scrolls and crosshatching. From Alaska before 1893. Gift of Lucien Wulsin, 1964.975.

21. **Bracelet,** silver, width .5, diameter about 7.0. Engraved foliate scrolls, crosshatching and rectangular motifs. From Alaska before 1893. Gift of Lucien Wulsin, 1964.976.

22. **Bracelet,** silver, width .8, diameter about 6.0. Engraved scrolls and lozenges. From Alaska before 1893. Gift of Lucien Wulsin, 1964.977.

23. **Bracelet,** silver, width 3.4, diameter about 6.5. Engraved eagle or thunderbird head and feathers, one end slotted to receive two hooks on other end; break repaired with applied strip of silver. From Alaska before 1893. Gift of Lucien Wulsin, 1964.969.

24. **Bracelet,** silver, width 2.3, diameter about 6.5. Engraved foliate scrolls, one end slotted to receive hook on other end. From Alaska before 1893. Gift of Lucien Wulsin, 1964.970.

25. **Bracelet,** silver, width 2.1, diameter about 6.0. Engraved foliate scrolls, one end slotted to receive hook on other end. From Alaska before 1893. Gift of Lucien Wulsin, 1964.971.

*26. **Headdress in the Form of a Frog,** carved and painted wood, height 21.5. From Alaska, 1892; partially obliterated inscription on reverse, "Ella Stebi s Cummins . . . Baker St. S.F. (S.P.?) . . . m Alaska June 1892 (?)." Gift of John W. Warrington, 1951.194.

*27. **Articulated Mask,** carved and painted wood with twisted bark and string cords for manipulation, height about 33.0. The eyes are pivoted and the lower jar is hinged with leather flaps. Source unknown, but from Northwest Coast before 1893. Gift of Lucien Wulsin, 1964.996.

*28. **Headdress Frontlet Mask,** carved and painted wood, height 17.8. Chilkat tribe, Alaska, 1889, said to have belonged to Skundoo, a Chilkat shaman. Gift of Dr. and Mrs. W. W. Seely, 1889.292.

29. **Headdress Frontlet Mask,** carved and painted wood, height 14.0. Chilkat tribe, Alaska, 1889, said to have belonged to Skundoo, a Chilkat shaman. Gift of Dr. and Mrs. W. W. Seeley, 1889.291.

*30. **Mask,** carved and painted wood, applied human hair and opercula set in as teeth, height 19.5. Probably a frontlet from a headdress; old vertical split mended with sinew. Chilkat tribe, Alaska,

1889, said to have belonged to Skundoo, a Chilkat shaman. Gift of Dr. and Mrs. W. W. Seely, 1889.294.

*31. **Mask,** carved and painted wood with applied sheet copper nostrils and eyelids, height 28.5. Eyes and mouth pierced, pegs surviving around mouth and eyebrows for applied material now missing. Chilkat tribe, Alaska, 1889, said to have belonged to Skundoo, a Chilkat shaman. Gift of Dr. and Mrs. W. W. Seely, 1889.295.

*32. **Headdress Frontlet Mask,** carved and painted wood with inlaid abalone shell, height 15.2. Chilkat tribe, Alaska, 1889, said to have belonged to Skundoo, a Chilkat shaman. Gift of Dr. and Mrs. W. W. Seely, 1889.290.

33. **Headdress Frontlet Mask,** carved and painted wood with inlaid abalone shell eyes, inset tooth or operculum, height 14.0. Chilkat tribe, Alaska, 1889, said to have been belonged to Skundoo, a Chilkat shaman. Gift of Dr. and Mrs. W. W. Seely, 1889.293.

*34. **Dagger,** iron or steel blade, wood hilt wrapped with twisted bark, pommel carved in the form of a head with inlaid shell eyes and nostril, length 46.2. Alaska before 1893. Gift of Lucien Wulsin, 1964.943.

*35. **Dagger,** iron or steel blade, wood hilt wrapped with hide thong and twisted bark, pommel carved in the form of a head, length 38.0. Sheath of blue-black trade cloth decorated with white trade beads, wood plug. From Alaska before 1906. Gift of William N. King, 1906.127.

36. **Double-Blade Dagger,** iron or steel blades, sheet copper blade sockets, grip bound with hide thong, length 58.5. From Alaska before 1893. Gift of Lucien Wulsin, 1964.942.

37. **Knife,** iron or steel blade lashed with textile strips to wood handle, length about 23.7. Used for carving the fine details on wood vessels and implements. From Alaska. Bequest of Harry Zerring, 1918.6390.

*38. **Mortar,** whale vertebra cut and incised to represent hawk and eagle heads, opercula set in rim, height 10.0. **Pestle,** white stone attached with metal band to carved and painted wood handle with bird's head finial, length 26.0. From Alaska, XIX c. Gift of Elizabeth Seely Espy and Grace Seely Groesbeck 1943.911.

*39. **Grease Dish in the Form of a Seal,** carved wood with oily patina, length 15.0. From British Columbia, Canada, before 1889, Bureau of Ethnology number 89155. Gift of the United States National Museum, 1889.87.

*40. **Cylindrical Vessel,** carved wood, length 48.3. From Alaska before 1893. Gift of Lucien Wulsin, 1964.950.

*41. **Bent Bowl,** carved wood with oily patina, opercula set in rim, height 13.0 by 30.0 by 17.3. The sides are formed from a single board kerfed, or scored, and bent at the corners, the ends lashed together with leather thongs. The bottom is a separate piece of wood, hollowed and ridged around the edge and pegged to the body. From Alaska before 1893. Gift of Lucien Wulsin, 1964.949.

*42. **Food Dish,** carved and painted wood, height 9.0 by 25.2 by 19.7. Carved from a block of wood, engraved masks on the ends, the sides plain and reeded at the corners. From Alaska before 1889, collected by James G. Swan, Bureau of Ethnology number 23482. Gift of the United States National Museum, 1889.85.

43. **Bowl,** carved wood and inlaid ivory (?) lozenges on rim, oily patina, 31.5 by 20.9. The rim and body are cut from separate pieces of wood. From Bristol Bay, Alaska, before 1889. Gift of the United States National Museum, 1889.82.

44. **Bowl,** carved wood, 27.1 by 19.1. Rim and body are carved from a single piece of wood. From "Kurkhpale" River, Alaska, before 1889, collected by E. W. Nelson, Bureau of Ethnology number 38684. Gift of the United States National Museum, 1889.81.

*45. **Surf Duck Dish,** carved and painted wood, length 38.5. Bottom flat except for duck's feet in relief. From Taku area, Alaska, before 1889, Bureau of Ethnology number 73748. Gift of the United States National Museum, 1889.88.

*46. **Dish,** mountain sheep horn molded and carved, height 13.6, length 21.6. From British Columbia, Canada, before 1893. Gift of Lucien Wulsin, 1964.951.

*47. **Scoop in the Form of a Duck,** mountain sheep horn molded and carved, height 12.4, length 18.0. Source unknown, but probably from Tlingit or Haida tribe, Alaska, or British Columbia, Canada. X-1965.15.

48. **Berry Spoon,** carved wood, length 42.1. From Alaska before 1893. Gift of Lucien Wulsin, 1964.962.

49. **Spoon,** carved wood, length about 22.8. Fine-grained, mottled wood, no decoration, polished surface. Haida tribe, Prince of Wales Island, Alaska, before 1889, collected by James G. Swan, Bureau of Ethnology number 20852. Gift of the United States National Museum, 1889.95.

50. **Spoon,** carved wood with traces of painted lines, length about 23.0. From Neah Bay, Washington, before 1889, probably Makah tribe, Bureau of Ethnology number 23337. Gift of the United States National Museum, 1889.97.

*51. **Ladle with Eagle Handle,** carved wood, length about 60.0. From Alaska, XX c. Gift of Amelia Dunham, 1948.9.

*52. **Spoon,** mountain goat horn with abalone shell inlay, length about 28.0. Handle carved with crest animals. Bowl and handle carved separately, now tied together but probably originally fastened with metal rivets. From Sitka, Alaska, before 1889. Gift of the United States National Museum, 1889.93.

53. **Spoon,** mountain goat horn handle, mountain sheep horn bowl, length about 31.8. Handle carved with crest animals. From Alaska before 1901. Gift of Mrs. H. S. Fechheimer, 1938.10622.

54. **Spoon,** mountain goat horn handle, mountain sheep horn bowl, metal rivets, length about 17.5. Handle carved with crest animals. Source unknown, but probably Tlingit or Haida tribe, Alaska or British Columbia. X-1959.26.

55. **Spoon,** mountain goat horn handle, mountain sheep horn bowl, metal rivets, length about 18.0. Handle carved with crest animals. Source unknown, but probably Tlingit or Haida tribe, Alaska or British Columbia. X-1959.27.

56. **Spoon,** mountain goat horn, length about 21.8. Handle carved with two heads of a long-beaked bird, one pointing upward as a finial, the other pointing down the back of the bowl. From Alaska before 1893. Gift of Lucien Wulsin, 1964.954.

57. **Spoon,** mountain goat horn handle, probably cattle horn bowl, length about 24.0. From Alaska before 1893. Gift of Lucien Wulsin, 1964.953.

58. **Spoon,** probably cattle horn, length about 25.5. Handle carved with crest animals. From Alaska, XIX c. Gift of Rebecca Scarborough and Mrs. Hugh Smythe, 1934.166.

*59. **Spoon,** probably cattle horn and abalone shell inlay, length about 30.5. Handle hollowed and cut out with crest animals carved as rings attached only at the back. From Alaska, XIX c. Gift of Rebecca Scarborough and Mrs. Hugh Smythe, 1934.167.

*60. **Halibut Hook,** carved wood, metal barb, twisted cedar bark cord, length about 28.5. One arm carved with raven (?) and another animal. From Alaska, probably Tlingit tribe, before 1906. Gift of William N. King, 1906.128.

61. **Halibut Hook,** carved wood, iron barb, split reed (?) binding, length about 26.5. One arm carved with hawk (?) figure. From Alaska, XIX c. Gift of Mrs. W. H. Taylor, 1924.248.

62. **Halibut Hook,** carved wood, iron barb, length about 26.5. One arm carved with a squid. From Alaska before 1893. Gift of Lucien Wulsin, 1964.945.

63. **Halibut (?) Hook,** carved wood, bone barb, length about 22.9. Two pieces, binding now missing, one arm carved with two beavers. From Alaska before 1893. Gift of Lucien Wulsin, 1964.946.

64. **Halibut Hook,** bent wood, iron barbs, split reed (?) binding, twisted bark cord, length about 38.0 From Alaska before 1893, probably Kwakiutl or Nootka tribe. Gift of Lucien Wulsin, 1964.948.

65. **Halibut Hook,** natural wood fork, iron barb, split reed (?) binding, length about 22.5. From Alaska before 1893. Gift of Lucien Wulsin, 1964.947.

*66. **Side of a Box,** carved and painted wood, 84.5 by 26.4. From Dr. B. K. Wilbur, Sitka, Alaska, said to be early XIX c. Gift of Mrs. William H. Taylor, 1923.843.

67. **Covered Box,** bent, painted and incised wood, twisted bark binding, height 14.5 by 14.9 by 14.5. The walls formed from a single thin board kerfed, or scored, and bent at the corners and pegged where the ends meet and to attach the bottom. The corners are painted with vertical stripes of magenta, the lid is incised in a simple criss-cross pattern, and a system of twisted bark cords twined together across the bottom and at intervals up the side once secured the lid, the cords being now broken and partly missing at the top. Source unknown, but from Northwest Coast. Bequest of Harry Zerring, 1918.6426.

68. **Small Totem Pole,** carved argillite, height 34.3. Source unknown, but probably from Haida tribe, Queen Charlotte Island, British Columbia, where the argillite was mined in the latter half of the XIX c. X-1968.3.

*69. **Small Totem Pole,** carved argillite, height 28.2. Haida tribe, Queen Charlotlle Island, British Columbia, XIX-XX c. Bequest of Charlotte H. Mackenzie, 1936.556.

70. **Small Totem Pole,** carved argillite, height 48.3. Haida tribe. Gift of William N. King, 1906.130.

71. **Flute,** carved argillite and applied ivory or bone, length 47.5. Haida tribe, Queen Charlotte Island, British Columbia, XIX-XX c. Gift of William Howard Doane, 1917.34.

*72. **Pipe,** carved argillite, length 24.4. In the form of a man on the back of a sea creature. Source unrecorded, but before 1894, probably from Haida tribe, Queen Charlotte Island, British Columbia, where the argillite was mined. Gift of Nettleton Neff, 1894.1258.

73. **Toy Canoe,** carved and painted wood, length 44.3. From Alaska before 1893. Gift of Lucien Wulsin, 1964.967.

74. **Pipe in the Form of a Bear's Paw,** carved wood and metal bowl, height 7.2. From Alsaka, XIX-XX c. Bequest of Harry Zerring, 1918.6394.

75. **Paint Brush,** wood, inlaid abalone shell, hair bristles, split reed (?) binding, length 20.7. From Alaska before 1893. Gift of Lucien Wulsin, 1964.-963.

*76. **Figure of a Man,** carved and painted cedar, applied hair and skin mantle and loincloth, height 47 without hair. Said to represent a Chilkat shaman. Gift of Mrs. Charles Fleischmann, 1911.1676.

*77. **Walrus Tusk Cribbage Board,** carved in relief, incised and colored, length 71.5. From Alaska. Gift of Samuel Ach, 1936.823.

78. **Semi-Circular Bag,** leather and fur piecework, 33 by 42.5. From Icy Cape, Arctic Coast, Alaska, XX c. Gift of Mrs. Kennon Dunham, 1923.860.

79. **Rectangular Bag,** leather and fur piecework, 21 by 59.5. Divided into three pockets with flaps at the top. From Icy Cape, Arctic Coast, Alaska, XX c. Gift of Mrs. Kennon Dunham, 1923.861.

80. **Bag,** leather and fur piecework, probably caribou skin, 58 by 32. Obleuk tribe, Alaska, XX c. Gift of Amelia Dunham, 1948.11.

81. **Man's Trousers with Feet,** buckskin with quills (worn off). Completely covering the body from the waist down, the buckskin had quillwork lines down center front legs and insteps and has quilled garter-bands fastened at knees. Probably from Athapaskan tribes, Alaska, XIX c. X-1976.2.

82. **Lance Head Bag,** fish skin and rawhide, height 24.2, diameter 7.8. Appliqued human figures and stripes, stiff base. From Sledge Island area, Alaska, XIX c. Gift of the United States National Museum, 1889.41.

83. **Basket with Lid,** willow,** height 13.0, diameter 15.4, coiled construction. From Yukon River area, Alaska, XIX c. Gift of W. N. King, 1906.131.

84. **Box with Lid,** grasses, height 10.0, diameter

**Botanical identification of basket fibers follows end of Catalogue Listing.*

11.0. Coiled construction with a band of openwork around the center. From Alaska. Gift of Mrs. S. Herbert Randall, 1911.1791.

85. **Cup with Handle,** folded birchbark with willow handle and edge, height 9.0, diameter 14.3. From Athapaskan area, Alaska, XIX c. Gift of Mrs. S. Herbert Randall, 1911.1794.

86. **Oval Bowl,** folded birchbark with willow edge, height 23.0 by 8.4 by 25.5. From Athapaskan area, Alaska, XIX c. Gift of James W. Bullock, 1907.150.

*87. **Basket,** grasses, woolen yarn and feathers, height 37.0, diameter 28.1. Modified openwork twining with pattern of false embroidered yarn and gull feathers caught with grasses, loops below braided rim and handles. From Aleutian Islands, XIX c. Gift of Mrs. H. S. Fechheimer, 1938.10618.

88. **Box with Lid,** grasses and woolen yarn, height 11.4, diameter 11.4. Twined construction with red, navy and blue yarn in scattered pattern. From Aleutian Islands, XIX c. Gift of W. N. King, 1906.-132.

89. **Basket,** spruce root and basket straws, height 28.0, diameter 25.5. Twined construction with false embroidered pattern of four eagles (?) with spread wings in grasses and stems of maidenhair fern. Tlingit tribe, XIX c. Gift of Mrs. Dudley V. Sutphin, 1934.42.

90. **Oval Basket on Rectangular Base,** spruce root and basket straws, height 12.9 by 25.5 by 16.8. Twined construction with bands of false embroidery. Tlingit tribe, XIX c. Gift of George W. Lewis for Annie K. Laws, 1928.235.

91. **Basket-Cup,** grasses and spruce root, height 11.4, diameter 7.6. Finely wrap-twined with overall geometric pattern in tans and browns. Tlingit tribe, XIX c. Gift of Mrs. H. S. Fechheimer, 1938.-10614.

92. **Basket-Cup,** spruce root and basket straws, height 10.8, diameter 8.2. Finely twined with bands of false embroidery in yellow and red. Tlingit tribe, XIX c. Gift of George W. Lewis for Annie K. Laws, 1928.236.

*93. **Basket,** spruce root and basket straws, height 19.8, diameter 21.7. Twined with false embroidery in geometric pattern. Tlingit tribe, Chilkat branch, XIX c., collected by James G. Swan, 1885. Gift of U. S. National Museum, 1889.46.

94. **Berry Basket,** spruce root and basket straws, height 8.8, diameter 12.6. Twined construction with false embroidery. Tlingit (?) tribe, XIX c. Gift of Mrs. S. Herbert Randall, 1911.1793.

95. **Basket,** spruce root and basket straws, height 10.1, diameter 12.6. Twined construction with false embroidered pattern of dyed straws. Tlingit tribe, late XIX or early XX c. Gift of Estate of William Watts Taylor, 1913.778.

96. **Basket,** spruce root, height 20.4, diameter 24.3. Twined with dark horizontal bands of overlay twining. Haida tribe, Queen Charlotte Island, XIX c. Gift of James W. Bullock, 1907.148.

97. **Rectangular Burden Basket,** cedar roots, squaw grass and cherry bark, height 29.2 by 38.2 by 33.2. Coiled construction with vertical pattern of imbrication on upper area, leather thongs. From Fraser River, British Columbia, XIX c. Gift of W. N. King, 1906.80.

98. **Rectangular Basket,** cedar roots, squaw grass and cherry bark, height 23 by 38.3 by 29.4. Coiled construction with imbricated vertical pattern. From Fraser River, British Columbia, XIX c. Gift of James W. Bullock, 1907.139.

99. **Box with Lid,** split cedar bark and grasses, height 9.5 by 12.8 by 10.3. Base of plain plaiting, body and lid wrap-twined with horizontal bands of purple and yellow. Makah tribe, Washington, probably XIX c. Gift of Estate of William Watts Taylor, 1913.781-782.

100. **Box with Lid,** split cedar bark and grasses, height 6.3, diameter 10.8. Base of plain plaiting, body and lid wrap-twined in multicolored bands. Makah tribe, Washington, late XIX or early XX c. Gift of Estate of William Watts Taylor, 1913.-779-780.

101. **Box with Lid,** split cedar bark and grasses, height 4.4, diameter 6.3. Base of plain plaiting, body and lid wrap-twined of grasses with colored stripes. Probably Makah tribe, XIX c. Gift of Mrs. H. S. Fechheimer, 1938.10617.

102. **Wallet,** sea grass and woolen yarn, 56.0 by 81.5. Sides twine-woven separately with red and blue yarn stripes, then joined with grass braids. Makah tribe, Washington, XIX c. Gift of United States National Museum, 1889.50.

103. **Berry Basket,** spruce or cedar root, cherry and cedar bark, height 15.1, diameter 15.1. Coiled construction with overall imbricated diagonal zigzags, slits around rim, fabric handle. Klikitat tribe, Washington, XIX c. Gift of W. N. King, 1906.81.

104. **Berry Basket,** pine roots and squaw grass, height 15.1, diameter 16.3. Twined construction with speckled pattern in wide band and twisted loops around rim. Quinault tribe, Washington, XIX c. Gift of James W. Bullock, 1907.131.

105. **Gathering Basket,** pine roots and squaw grass, height 27.5, diameter 30.7. Twined construction with overall light and dark pattern, two thong loops. Quinault tribe, Washington, XIX c. Gift of James W. Bullock, 1907.125.

106. **Clam or Utility Basket,** rectangular, height 26.8 by 38.3 by 23.0. Open twining with rope handles. From Puget Sound area, XIX c. Gift of James W. Bullock, 1907.138.

107. **Utility Basket,** oval, birch withes, height 23 by 29.3 by 14.1. Twilled-plaited splints with added scalloped edge. Clallam tribe, Washington, XIX c., collected by James G. Swan, 1876. Gift of United States National Museum, 1889.49.

108. **Clam Basket,** cedarbark, height 14.0, diameter 30.8. Coiled construction with imbricated pattern. Umatilla tribe, Oregon, XIX c. Gift of W. N. King, 1906.72.

California

109. **Basket-Hat,** hazel roots, sourgrass and maidenhair fern, height 9.0, diameter 18.0. Twined construction with geometric "flint" design. Hupa tribe, XIX c. Gift of Mrs. S. Herbert Randall, 1911.1797.

110. **Oval Carrier Basket,** willow, 43.4 by 56 by 35.8. Openwork twining with a wicker base and a design of close twining near the top with a braided edge, red cloth loops. Hupa tribe, XIX c. Gift of James W. Bullock, 1907.134.

*111. **Basket-Bowl,** sourgrass, maidenhair and woodwardia ferns, height 18.0, diameter 22.9. Twined construction with a stepped geometric pattern. Probably Hupa tribe, XX c. Gift of Amelia Elizabeth White, 1937.507.

112. **Basket-Hat,** work-hat type, hazel roots and sourgrass, height 8.4, diameter 17.9. Twined construction with minor pattern of small x's. Hupa tribe, California, XIX c. Gift of James W. Bullock, 1907.174.

*113. **Baby Carrier,** willow 77.5 by 37.0. Plain openwork twining with horizontal rows of wrapped twining, the bottom lined with shredded cedarbark for the baby to sit on. Shown with Cat. No. 114 as a protective cap. Hupa tribe, California, XIX c. Gift of James W. Bullock, 1907.122.

*114. **Strainer-Basket,** Western Juniper, diameter 28.0. Openwork twined construction with three stripes of color coming from center. Shown as a protective cap over Cat. No. 113. Klamath or Yurok tribe, California, XIX c. Gift of W. N. King, 1906.153.

115. **Basket-Bowl,** tule, height 16.7, diameter 53.5. Twined construction with geometric pattern of mud-dyed fibers. Klamath tribe, Northern California and Southern Oregon, XIX c. Gift of James W. Bullock, 1907.170.

116. **Basket,** hazelnut stick warps and conifer roots, sourgrass, and woodwardia fern wefts, height 16.7, diameter 25.5. Two and three strand twining with overlay geometric design. Yurok tribe, Weitchpec, Klamath River, California, XIX c. Gift of James W. Bullock, 1907.168.

117. **Winnowing Basket-Bowl,** hazelnut sticks with sourgrass and woodwardia fern, height 15.4, diameter 60.0. Twined construction with bands of alder-dyed woodwardia fern. Yurok tribe, Weitchpec, XIX c. Gift of James W. Bullock, 1907.173.

118. **Barrel-Shaped Basket,** hazelnut sticks, sourgrass and woodwardia fern, height 10.1, diameter 16.4. Twined construction with vertical stepped design and openwork just below wrapped edge. Probably Yurok tribe, XIX c. Gift of W. N. King, 1906.118.

119. **Basket,** hazelnut sticks, sourgrass, maidenhair and woodwardia fern, height 12.3, diameter 20.5. Twined construction with geometric "flying geese" design. Yurok tribe, late XIX or early XX c. Gift of Estate of William Watts Taylor, 1913.773.

120. **Basket-Hat,** sourgrass and woodwardia fern, height 9.0, diameter 17.3. Twined construction with geometric "flint" design. Yurok tribe, late XIX or early XX c. Gift of Estate of William Watts Taylor, 1913.775.

121. **Basket,** sourgrass with maidenhair and woodwardia fern, height 16.7, diameter 20.5. Twined construction with geometric pattern. Yurok tribe, late XIX or early XX c. Gift of Estate of William Watts Taylor, 1913.774.

122. **Hopper-Basket,** sedge grass roots, redbud (?), height 18.0, diameter 49.7. Three-ply braid start with twined construction and wide band of three-strand weaving, thick wood splint lashed around rim. Acorn grinding was done through the hole in center bottom. Pomo tribe, California, XIX c. Gift of W. N. King, 1906.142.

123. **Basket-Bowl,** sedge grass roots, redbud bark, height, 12.2, diameter 53.5. Twined construction with horizontal band and sections of three-strand weaving, uncut bams around rim. Pomo tribe, California, XIX c. Gift of James W. Bullock, 1907.185.

124. **Cooking Basket,** sedge grass roots, redbud bark, height 18.0, diameter 37.0. Twined con-

struction with geometric pattern. Probably Pomo tribe, California, XX c. Gift of Amelia Elizabeth White, 1937.508.

125. **Basket,** sedge grass roots, redbud bark, height 15.5, diameter 18.5. Twill-twined and twill-wicker construction with "arrowhead" pattern, uncut bams around rim. Probably Pomo tribe, California, XIX c. Gift of James W. Bullock, 1907.178.

126. **Basket,** sedge grass roots, redbud bark, willow, meadowlark feathers, glass overlay beads, height 11.5, diameter 28.0. Coiled construction with diagonal pattern and bits of remaining feathers and beads at top. Pomo tribe, California, XIX c. Bequest of Eleanor I. Earnshaw, 1912.360.

127. **Oval Basket,** sedge grass roots, redbud bark, willow, clam shell disks and trade beads, quail plumes, 10.8 by 31.8 by 20.4. Coiled construction with pattern of squares and added trim. Pomo tribe, California, XIX c. Gift of W. N. King, 1906.146.

128. **Storage Basket,** sedge grass roots, redbud bark, willow and clam shell disks, height 38.2, diameter 80.2. Coiled construction with geometric spiral pattern and tipped with disks and remnants of feathers. Pomo tribe, California, XIX c. Bequest of Eleanor I. Earnshaw, 1912.351.

129. **Gift or Jewel Basket,** sedge grass roots, redbud bark, willow, clam shell disks and trade beads, height 7.8, diameter 18.5. Three-rod coiled construction with geometric pattern accented with glass beads; shell disks on string handle. Pomo tribe, California, XIX c. Gift of W. N. King, 1906.147.

130. **Gift or Jewel Basket,** sedge grass roots, willow, clam shell disks and trade beads with abalone pendants, height 5.2, diameter 11.0. Three-rod coiled construction with no pattern, disks around rim and on sinew handle, chalk white bead pendants. Pomo tribe, California, XIX c. Gift of W. N. King, 1906.148.

131. **Basket,** sedge grass roots, redbud bark, willow, clam shell disks and trade beads, height 7.8, diameter 21.7. Coiled construction with geometric pattern accented with chalk white trade beads, disks around rim. Pomo tribe, California, XIX c. Gift of W. N. King, 1906.149.

132. **Gift Basket,** sedge grass roots, redbud bark, willow, clam shell disks and trade beads, woodpecker feathers and quail plumes, height 11.5, diameter 20.4. Coiled construction, "arrowhead" design accented with chalk white trade beads and feathers, disks on rim and handle. Pomo tribe, California, XIX c. Bequest of Eleanor I. Earnshaw, 1912.353.

*133. **Oval Basket,** sedge grass roots, redbud bark, willow, pendants of red and navy trade beads and clam shell disks, 9.0 by 30.6 by 23.0. Coiled construction with horizontal zigzag lines accented by the pendants, additional disks on rim. Pomo tribe, California, XIX c. Bequest of Eleanor I. Earnshaw, 1212.358.

134. **Basket,** sedge grass roots, redbud bark, willow, clam shell disks and trade beads, and quail plumes, height 14.0, diameter 34.4. Coiled construction, diagonal geometric pattern with chalk white beads and remnants of feathers on upper part, groups of disks and plumes along rim. Pomo tribe, California, XIX c. Bequest of Eleanor I. Earnshaw, 1912.363.

*135. **Ceremonial Basket,** sedge grass roots, redbud bark, willow, woodpecker and hummingbird (?) feathers, clam shell disks, trade bead and abalone shell pendants, height 10.3, diameter 25.5. Coiled construction with diamond shapes outlined along inside rim, outside completely covered with zigzag patterns of red and black feathers accented with pendants, a row of disks on rim. Pomo tribe, XIX c. Bequest of Eleanor I. Earnshaw, 1912.352.

136. **Basket,** sedge grass roots, redbud bark, willow, trade beads, height 19.2, diameter 35.7. Coiled construction, geometric pattern with overlay triangular design of chalk white beads and remnants of feathers. Probably Pomo tribe, California, XIX c. Bequest of Eleanor I. Earnshaw, 1912.354.

137. **Sieve-Basket,** hazel or willow, height 15.5, diameter 43.3. Openwork wicker plaiting with coils of shoots forming the rim. Pomo tribe, Kulanapo branch, California, XIX c. Gift of James W. Bullock, 1907.182.

138. **Basket-Bowl,** for drying fish, hazel or willow, height 7.8, diameter 25.5. Openwork wicker plaiting with coils of shoots forming the rim. Pomo tribe, Kulanapo branch, California, XIX c. Gift of James W. Bullock, 1907.183.

139. **Fish-Scoop Basket,** hazel or willow, height 15.5, diameter 25.5, length of handle 18. Openwork wicker plaiting with bunch of shoots self-wrapped to form the handle. Pomo tribe, Kulanapo branch, California, XIX c. Gift of James W. Bullock, 1907.179.

140. **Basket-Tray,** for meal, sedge grass roots, redbud, height 14.3, diameter 20.6. Twined construction, entirely done in overlay three-strand weave in a horizontal striped pattern. Pomo tribe, Kulanapo branch, California, XIX c. Gift of James W. Bullock, 1907.184.

141. **Baby Carrier,** willow, height 43.5, diameter 27.0. Vines and twigs held together in "U" shape by twined and braided cord, a heavy splint lashed horizontally at top. Pomo tribe, Kulanapo branch, California, XIX c. Gift of James W. Bullock, 1907.180.

142. **Basket-Bowl,** grasses, cladium root and blackfern root, height 16.0, diameter 35.8. Coiled construction with diagonal "flying geese" pattern. Yokuts tribe, Tulare area, California, XIX c. Gift of W. N. King, 1906.135.

143. **Bottle-Basket,** grasses, cladium roots, blackfern root, redbud, height 12.8, diameter 21.7. Coiled construction with three bands of "rattlesnake" pattern. From Tulare area, California, XIX c. Gift of W. N. King, 1906.137.

144. **Basket,** grasses, cladium root, blackfern root height 33.2, diameter 61.0. Coiled construction with 2 bands of "rattlesnake" pattern. Yokuts tribe, Tulare area, California, XIX c. Gift of W. N. King, 1906.133.

145. **Bottle-Basket,** grasses, cladium root, blackfern root, wool fringe, quail plumes, height 10.8, diameter 17.3. Coiled construction with 2 bands of "rattlesnake" pattern and red fringe and plumes around the shoulder-ridge. Yokuts tribe, Tulare area, California, XIX c. Bequest of Eleanor I. Earnshaw, 1912.362.

146. **Bottle-Basket,** grasses, cladium root, blackfern root, redbud, height 12.2, diameter 16.7. Coiled construction with pattern of horizontal zigzags. Yokuts tribe, Tulare area, California, XIX c. Bequest of Eleanor I. Earnshaw, 1912.361.

147. **Basket-Bowl,** grasses, cladium root, blackfern root, redbud, height 16.0, diameter 43.3. Coiled construction with patterns of zigzags and short horizontal lines. Yokuts tribe, Tulare area, California, XIX c. Gift of James W. Bullock, 1907.171.

148. **Basket,** grasses, cladium root, blackfern root, redbud, height 16.6, diameter 35.7. Coiled construction with "rattlesnake" pattern and human figures. Yokuts tribe, Tulare area, California, XIX c. Bequest of Eleanor I. Earnshaw, 1912.359.

*149. **Basket-Bowl,** grasses, cladium root, blackfern root, redbud, height 16.6, diameter 41.5. Coiled construction with pattern of vertical bands forming panels containing medallions and a human figure. Yokuts tribe, Tulare area, California, XIX c. Gift of W. N. King, 1906.134.

150. **Oval Dance or Friendship Basket,** grasses,

cladium root, blackfern root, 9.0 by 23.0 by 15.4. Coiled construction with continuous pattern of human figures holding hands. Yokuts tribe, Tulare area, California, XIX c. Gift of W. N. King, 1906.90.

151. **Oval Dance or Friendship Basket,** grasses, cladium root, blackfern root, redbud 11.5 by 38.2 by 25.5. Coiled construction with continuous pattern of human figures holding hands. Yokuts tribe, King's County, California, XIX c. Gift of W. N. King, 1906.91.

152. **Basket-Bowl,** willow and redbud, height 13.0, diameter 30.0. Coiled construction with triangle pattern in checkerboard effect. Wailaki tribe, Sacramento Valley, XIX c. Gift of James W. Bullock, 1907.186.

153. **Basket-Tray** (for grinding), willow and redbud, height 6.5, diameter 40.8. Coiled construction with pattern of six-pointed "star." Wintun tribe, Nomlaki branch, Northern California, XIX c. Gift of James W. Bullock, 1907.151.

154. **Basket-Bowl,** willow and redbud, height 10.2, diameter 28.0. Coiled construction with "flying geese" pattern. Wintun tribe, California, XIX c. Gift of W. N. King, 1906.150.

155. **Berry Basket,** grasses and juncus rush, height 9.0, diameter 16.7. Coiled construction with darker diagonal pattern. Cahuilla tribe, Mission group, Southern California, XIX c. Gift of W. N. King, 1906.82.

156. **Basket-Bowl,** grasses and juncus rush, height 10.3, diameter 28.8. Coiled construction with pattern of diagonal lines and vertical diamonds. From Mission group, San Diego, Southern California, XIX c. Gift of James W. Bullock, 1907.132.

157. **Basket,** grasses and juncus rush, height 10.2, diameter 42.0. Coiled construction with color patches. From Mission group, San Diego, Southern California, XIX c. Gift of George W. Lewis for Annie K. Laws, 1928.243.

The Plains

*158. **Painted Buffalo Hide,** approximately 209.0 by 218. Once the property of Standing Buffalo, a Sioux chief, painted with symbols of events and forces significant in his life; acquired by the donor in 1871 from Benjamin Potts, Governor of the Territory of Montana, who acquired it through an agent from Chief Standing Buffalo shortly before the latter was killed in a battle with the Gros Ventres north of the Missouri River. Gift of General M. F. Force, 1894.1209.

159. **Painted Buffalo Hide,** approximately 340.0 by 260.0. Scene of mounted warriors and soldiers. Said to be from Cheyenne tribe, Montana, XIX c. Gift of F. H. Huntington, 1897.13.

160. **Painted and Beaded Buffalo Hide,** approximately 240.0 by 200.0. Painted with repeated geometric motif that may represent feather clusters; a multicolor strip of beading down the center. Said to be Arapahoe origin, XIX c. Gift of General M. F. Force, 1894.1208.

161. **A Sun Dance Ceremony and Mounted Warriors,** said to be by Black Chicken, Northern Plains, painting on muslin, height 176.5, width 277. Once in the collection of Dale O. Cowen, Fort Peck, Poplar Creek Indian Agency, Montana. Gift of Mrs. Philip C. Swing 1942.91.

*162. **Mounted Warriors, Soldiers and Amorous Couples,** said to be by Wakankdimaza, Sioux tribe, XIX c., painting on muslin, height 176.0, width 230.0. Said of have been used as a tent liner. Gift of General M. F. Force, 1894.1214.

163. **Mounted Warriors,** painting on muslin, approximately 91 by 91.0. Said to have been obtained from a Southern Cheyenne tribe in Oklahoma, XIX c. Purchased from J. H. Sharp, 1899.80.

164. **Animals, Figures and Signs,** probably a winter count, ink (?) on muslin, 92.0 by 92.0. Said to have been drawn by a member of the Two Kettle Band Sioux, Nebraska, XIX c. Gift of General M. F. Force, 1894.1248.

165. Big Bow Surrounded by Navajos

166. Sun Boy Dancing Before his Lodge

*167. Fox Skin Bonnet Returning to his Lodge

168. Medicine Dance

169. A Kiowa Chief Getting up a War Party

170. **Kiowas and Navajos Preparing for a Fight** Colored drawings, pencil and colored crayons on paper, height 15.8, width 25.2. Descriptive captions written on the mounts, probably by donor's grandfather, Merritt Barber, who collected them from Kiowa tribe when he was an army officer at Fort Sill and other posts west of the Mississippi around 1880. Gift of Merritt Boyle, 1954.196-.197, .202-.205.

*171. **Feather Bonnet,** feathers, beads, cloth and fur, height approximately 206.0. Base of each golden eagle tail feather bound with red trade cloth, sheep's wool cap with centered Sun Dance plume, beaded band at front and white ermine strips at sides. Cheyenne tribe, XIX c. Gift of General M. F. Force, 1894.1227.

172. **Feather Bonnet,** feathers, beads and fur, height approximately 75.0. Beaded band, erect crest of golden eagle tail feathers, strips of white ermine hanging from the sides. Blackfeet tribe, XIX c. Gift of General M. F. Force, 1894.1226.

173. **Bonnet Box,** for headdresses and other ceremonial objects, painted rawhide, length 39.7, diameter 10.3. Red and green geometric painted pattern with horizontal rows of thong-tied tin cones. From Montana area, probably Blackfeet or Crow tribe, XIX c. Gift of Mrs. Nettleton Neff, 1940.1238.

174. **Dress,** buckskin with beads, 129.0 from center neck to ankles. Sides seamed, open sleeves, self fringe along sides and bottom with some fur tips, deer tail at center front and back chest, band of lazy-stitch beadwork across chest and top sleeves. Crow tribe, Montana, XIX c. Gift of General M. F. Force, 1894.1211.

*175. **Dress,** buckskin with beads, 142.0 from center neck to ankles. Sides seamed, open sleeves, self-fringe along bottom, sleeve has some fur tips, wide yoke of lazy-stitch beadwork. Crow or Sioux tribe, late XIX or early XX c. X-1975.29.

176. **Woman's Leggings,** beaded buckskin with replaced (?) cotton, length 52.0. White lazy-stitch beadwork with multicolor geometric pattern in a band around the bottom and up the sides. Sioux or Crow tribe, XIX c. Gift of Mrs. O. E. Hilmer, 1973.537a, b.

177. **Woman's Leggings,** beaded buckskin, length 29.4. Solid lazy-stitch beadwork, white with multicolored pattern, thong lacing on sides. Cheyenne or Sioux tribe, XIX c. Gift of Amelia Elizabeth White, 1937.547.

178. **Shirt,** buckskin, 83.0 from center neck to bottom. Long narrow closed sleeves, sides seamed, long, twisted fringe on neck flaps, shoulders, and across the shirt, slight rubbed color on the neck flap. From Southern Plains area, possibly Kiowa or Arapahoe tribe, XX (?) c. Gift of Amelia Elizabeth White, 1937.539.

179. **Shirt,** European style, elkskin, 83.0 from center neck to bottom. Open sides and long sleeves, fringe edging and minor trim of beads and fringe with red trade cloth binding. From Northern Plains area, XX c. Gift of Amelia Elizabeth White, 1937.540.

*180. **Ceremonial Shirt,** colored buckskin, beads and trade cloth, 96.0 from center neck to bottom. Horizontal brown lines are impressed all over, blue pigment rubbed on left side, green on right side, lazy-stitch beaded bands on sleeves and upper sides, neck flaps of red and navy cloth, sides and undersleeves are open. Blackfeet tribe, XIX c. Gift of General M. F. Force, 1894.20.

*181. **Man's Leggings,** beaded buckskin and trade cloth, length approximately 100.0. Yellow buckskins, impressed brown horizontal lines, vertical beaded bands on sides, red cloth around bottom. Blackfeet tribe, XIX c. Gift of General M. F. Force, 1894.21, .22.

182. **Man's Leggings,** army blanket cloth with beads and trade cloth, length 37.0. Beaded bands with red cloth binding around ankles, possibly from Crow tribe, XIX c. From Fort Buford on Montana-North Dakota line. Gift of General M. F. Force, 1894.147, .148.

183. **Vest,** solidly beaded buckskin. Lazy-stitch beadwork, predominantly white with metallic and multicolored seed beads, buckskin thong ties. From Northern Plains, possibly Crow tribe, XIX c. Gift of Amelia Elizabeth White, 1937.537.

*184. **Vest,** buckskin with quillwork. Stylized floral design in colored two-thread quillwork on front, purple cotton back, thong ties. Probably from Northern Plains, late XIX or early XX c. Gift of Amelia Elizabeth White, 1937.536.

185. **Ghost Dance Shirt for the religious** ceremony celebrating the faith in the coming of an Indian Messiah, painted muslin, 90.0 from center neck to bottom. Fringed white cotton with sparse multi-colored designs painted on front, long sleeves. Probably from Teton Sioux tribe, 1890-1891. Gift of Reverend William Roeper, 1896.21.

186. **Breechcloth** (?), trade cloth, wool yarn, beads and buckskin, 137.0 by 21.7. Ends of red cloth have horizontal rows of beading with green yarn tufts and buckskin fringe. From the Plains, XIX c. Gift of General M. F. Force, 1894.23.

187. **Pair of Cuffs,** buckskin with quills, depth 20.5. Flared, stylized floral pattern quillwork, yellow calico binding, thong ties. From the Plains, XX c. Gift of Amelia Elizabeth White, 1937.550., .551.

188. **Pair of Cuffs,** beaded leather, depth 14.3. Solidly covered with lazystitch beadwork, predominantly white, with geometric pattern, calico lining, thong ties. From the Plains, XX c. Gift of Amelia Elizabeth White, 1937.548, .549.

189. **Moccasins,** painted buckskin, beads, rawhide soles, length 26.0. From Blackfeet tribe, XIX c. Gift of General M. F. Force, 1894.24, .25.

190. **Moccasins,** beaded buckskin, rawhide soles, length 25. Tops solidly covered with multicolored beads in geometric (buffalo track pattern) patterns, double-pointed tongue with tin cone and feather tassels. Probably Crow tribe, XIX c. Gift of Estate of Nettleton Neff, 1940.1223, .1224.

191. **Ceremonial Moccasins,** beaded buckskin, length 25.0. Top and sole solidly covered with lazy-stitch beadwork in predominately white and green geometric pattern with cone and feather tassel on tongue. Probably Cheyenne tribe, XIX c. Gift of Mrs. O. E. Hilmer, 1973.540.

192. **Moccasins,** buckskin, beads, fabric, rawhide sole, yellow and red pigment, length 25.5. Beaded band around sole and on front, printed cotton and red trade cloth cuffs, long fringe in back. From Northern Plains area, possibly Cheyenne tribe, XIX c. Gift of General M. F. Force, 1894.97, .98.

193. **Moccasins,** colored buckskin, beads, rawhide soles, length 25.5. Leather pigmented yellow, green, red and navy, narrow bands of white beads, leather fringe on uppers and heels. From Southern Plains, possibly Kiowa or Comanche tribe, XIX c. Gift of General M. F. Force, 1894-.106-107.

*194. **Moccasins,** beaded buckskin, rawhide soles, length 24.5. Yellow pigmented leather almost entirely covered with beads in stripes of green and white with red and navy motifs. Probably Cheyenne tribe, XIX c. Gift of General M. F. Force, 1894.104-105.

195. **Moccasins,** buckskin, beads and trade cloth, length 24.0. Soft soled, the front solidly covered with multicolored beadwork, bands of red and navy wool at the cuff. From the northwest Plains, XIX c. Gift of Mrs. W. O. Owen, 1938.10633.

196. **Child's Moccasins,** beaded buckskin, rawhide soles, length 16.5. Tops solidly covered with navy and white trade beads in lazy-stitch, plain cuffs. Sioux tribe, XIX c. Gift of Nettleton Neff, 1940.1225-1226.

*197. **Woman's Legging-Moccasins,** buckskin, dyed porcupine quills, rawhide soles, height 13.2, length 26.0. Orange and red quillwork in floral and bird patterns, thong-ties, cotton lining. From Southern Plains, XIX c. Gift of Estate of Nettleton Neff, 1940.1227, .1228.

198. **Belt and Pouch,** beaded buckskin and commercial leather, width of belt 5.2, pouch 12.8 by 10.3. Belt solidly covered with pink and blue lazy-stitch beading, leather ends, metal buckle; buckskin pouch flap solidly covered with overlay beadwork in 4-petal design. From Northern Plains, possibly Crow tribe, XIX c. Purchased from Samuel Buckley and Co., 1887.46.

199. **Belt and Pouch,** beaded buckskin, width of belt 3.8, pouch 10.3 by 12.8 with flap 39.0 long. Band of buckskin holds the pouch, the flap of which is solidly covered with overlay beadwork in geometric pattern. Probably Crow tribe, XIX c. Gift of General M. F. Force, 1894.1084.

200. **Bag,** buckskin with beads, 24.2 by 15.4. Two tones of smoked yellow buckskin with geometric designs of yellow and blue beadwork, beaded tassels. From Northern Plains, possibly Blackfeet tribe, probably early XX c. Gift of Mrs. A. H. Chatfield, 1936.593.

201. **Bag,** beaded buckskin, 25.5 by 16.7. Front solidly beaded in lazy-stitch in geometric pattern. From the Plains, probably Cheyenne or Blackfeet tribe, XIX c. or early XX c. Gift of Mrs. O. E. Hilmer, 1973.538.

202. **Bag, buckskin,** dyed porcupine quills, beads and cowhide with hair, 43.3 by 19.2. Beaded bands on both sides, quillwork on front, back cowhide, wrapped quillwork fringe at bottom with tin cones and red horsehair. Sioux tribe, XIX c. Gift of Estate of Nettleton Neff, 1940.1222.

203. **"Strike-A-Light" Bag,** commercial leather with beads, 12.8 by 8.4. Beaded geometric patterns, fringe of tin cones on bottom and flap. From Southern Plains, probably early XX c. Used by women to hold fire-making equipment. Gift of Mrs. A. H. Chatfield, 1936.592.

204. **Awl Case,** commercial leather with beads, length 19.0. Awl-shaped with a sliding top, solidly covered with beadwork. Source unknown, X-1976.3.

205. **Bag,** commercial leather with beads, 20.0 by 4.0. Lazy-stitch beadwork in geometric pattern, sliding top. From Plains, XIX c. Used by women to hold whetstone. Gift of Mrs. W. O. Owen, 1938.10637.

206. **Bag,** buckskin with beads, 38.3 by 10.3. Stiff skin, pony beads at top, seed beads in a band at sides and bottom, quill-wrapped buckskin fringe. Blackfeet tribe, XIX c. Gift of Dr. S. C. Heighway, 1937.7619.

*207. **Bag,** buckskin with beads and quills, 44.7 by 15.5. Beadwork bands at top and bottom with fringe hanging from quill-wrapped rawhide strips. Blackfeet tribe, XIX c. Gift of General M. F. Force, 1894.1205.

208. **Bag,** buckskin with beads and quills, 40.8 by 15.0. Yellow buckskin, bands of lazy-stitch beadwork, quill-wrapped rawhide strips and fringe at bottom. Sioux tribe, Dakota, XIX c. Gift of Dr. S. C. Heighway, 1937.7618.

209. **Bag,** buckskin with beads, 46.0 by 12.8. Yellow buckskin, bands of beadwork in geometric pattern, fringe at bottom and flap at top. Probably Dakota or Cheyenne tribe, XIX c. Gift of General M. F. Force, 1894.1243.

210. **Bag,** trade cloth, beads and fringe, 43.3 by 14.0. Red cloth, narrow bands and floral pattern in multicolored beadwork with band of loom-beadwork at the bottom from which hang tin cones, cloth and twisted leather fringe. Probably from Dakota area, XIX c. Gift of General M. F. Force, 1894.1231.

211. **Bag,** buffalo hide with beads, 47.5 by 20.5. Yellow leather with bands of predominately white lazy-stitch beadwork and some tin cones, quill-wrapped rawhide strips and leather fringe at bottom. Probably Sioux or Cheyenne tribe, XX c. Gift of Amelia Elizabeth White, 1937.560.

212. **Bag,** buckskin with beads, 40.7 by 15.5. Yellow buckskin, beaded bands, four flaps at top and leather fringe at bottom. Probably Dakota tribe, XIX c. Gift of General M. F. Force, 1894.1244.

213. **Bag,** buckskin with quillwork, 45.7 by 15.4. Band of multicolored quillwork in geometric pattern, quill-wrapped rawhide and fringe at the bottom. Dakota tribe, XIX c. Gift of General M. F. Force, 1894.1245.

214. **Knife Sheath,** buckskin-covered rawhide with beads, 25.5 by 9.0. Edged with band of multicolored trade beads and long fringe. Blackfeet tribe, XIX c. Gift of General M. F. Force, 1894.1247.

215. **Knife Sheath,** buckskin-covered rawhide with beads, 25.5 by 7.0. Multicolored beads in a geometric pattern and beaded tassel with quill-wrapped fringe. Probably Blackfeet tribe, XIX c. Gift of General M. F. Force, 1894.1083.

216. **Knife Sheath,** buckskin-covered rawhide with beads, 25.5 by 7.7. Entirely covered with multicolored lazy-sitch beading in geometric patterns. Sioux tribe, Dakota, XIX c. Gift of Lucien Wulsin, 1964.982.

*217. **Knife Sheath,** painted rawhide with beads, 28.8 by 9.0. Front daubed with red pigment, buckskin cuff has beaded geometric pattern. Sioux tribe, Dakota, XIX c. Gift of General M. F. Force, 1894.1232.

218. **Knife Sheath,** elkskin with quills, 25.5 by 9.0. Front solidly covered with colored 2-thread quillwork, back has narrow stripes of quillwork. Probably Sioux tribe, XIX c. Gift of Estate of Nettleton Neff, 1940.1232.

219. **Bracelet,** probably German silver, width .7, decorated with incised lines. Source unknown, but probably from the Plains before 1880. Gift of Thomas Cleneay, 1887.20662.

220. **Child's (?) Breastplate,** dentalium shell, rawhide and brass studs, 18.5 by 16.5. Horizontal rows of shells on rawhide spaced by vertical bands of studs. From the Plains, XIX c. Gift of General M. F. Force, 1894.1216.

221. **Breastplate,** hairpipes (cattle bones), French brass trade beads, leather, Indian head pennies, 90.0 by 23.0. Vertical rows of "pipes," spaced with horizontal leather, fringe of brass beads tipped with pennies (from 1864-1902). From Northern Plains, XX c. Gift of Mrs. Frank Perin, 1918.5049.

222. **Ceremonial Hair Ornament,** beaded buckskin, rawhide, owl feathers, horsehair, 79.0 by 7.5. White band of beadwork with red and blue pattern, four beaded thongs attached to the sides, feathers and long grey horsehair hanging from the bottom. Sioux tribe, XX c. Gift of Amelia Elizabeth White, 1937.555.

*223. **Man's Ceremonial Pad Saddle,** buckskin with beads and processed leather. Corners overlay beaded in floral pattern, European-style leather straps and stirrups. **Saddle Cloth,** trade cloth with beads, 98.1 by 76.4. Navy wool with corners overlay beaded in floral pattern. From Fort Buford area, possible Crow tribe, XIX c. Gift of General M. F. Force, 1894.145, .146.

224. **Saddle Cloth,** beaded buckskin and cotton, 158.0 by 58.6. Predominately white lazy-stitch beadwork covers the long panels of the cotton "H", "hawk" bells attached. Sioux or Cheyenne tribe, late XIX or early XX c. Gift of Amelia Elizabeth White, 1937.562.

225. **Pair of Saddle Bags,** beaded elkskin, 38.0 by 65.0. Fronts have white lazy-stitch beadwork with yellow and green diamonds, tin cones, thong-tied flaps. From Northern Plains, probably Teton Sioux, XIX c. Gift of Joseph H. Sharp, 1930.382, .383.

226. **Pair of Saddle Bags,** beaded elkskin, 30.0 by 54.0. Fronts solidly beaded in lazy-stitch, predominately blue, tin cones and thong-tied flaps. From Northern Plains, probably Sioux XX c. Gift of Amelia Elizabeth White, 1937.558, .559.

227. **Saddle Bag,** beaded buckskin and canvas, 109.0 by 38.0. Pocket at each end has multicolored lazy-stitch beadwork and fringe, cotton canvas backing. Sioux tribe, XIX c. Gift of Nettleton Neff, 1940.1238.

228. **Bow Case and Quiver,** buckskin with beads, length of quiver 63.7, bow case 91.8. Each has beaded bands of squares, buckskin fringe. Northern Arapahoe tribe, XIX c. Gift of General M. F. Force, 1894.1015.

*229. **Bow Case and Quiver,** buckskin with beads, length of quiver 63.7, bow case 102.0. Each has multicolored lazy-stitch beadwork and red trade cloth with yellow-dyed leather fringe; strap is buffalo fur on one side, trade cloth on the other. Blackfeet tribe, XIX c. Gift of General M. F. Force, 1894.27.

230. **Bow Case and Quiver,** buckskin, trade cloth and beads, length of quiver 71.2, bow case 109.5. Each has red cloth with borders of navy and white beads and buckskin fringe at bottom. Probably Sioux tribe, XIX c. Gift of Joseph H. Sharp, 1905.364, .365.

231. **Bow Case and Quiver,** buckskin with beads, length of quiver 76.3, bow case 91.8. Each has stripes of blue and red beads and buckskin fringe with otter fur strap. From Northern Plains, XIX c. Purchased from Samuel Buckley and Co., 1887.47.

*232. **Quiver,** fur, cloth, and beadwork, length 81.5, width 23.0, fringe 38.3. Weasel (?) fur and red trade cloth with multicolored floral beadwork. Blackfeet tribe, XIX c. Gift of General M. F. Force, 1894.64.

233. **Child's Bow Case and Quiver,** buckskin with beads, length of quiver 34.5, bow case 51.0. Each has borders of white, navy and yellow beads with buckskin fringe. From Plains, XIX c. Gift of Nettleton Neff, 1940.1235.

234. **Gun Case,** buckskin with beads, 102.0 by 17.8. Multicolored lazy-stitch beadwork in geometric pattern on front, diagonal lines on back, buckskin fringe. Cheyenne tribe, Wyoming, XIX c. Gift of General M. F. Force, 1894.99.

235. **Gun Case,** buckskin with beads, 61.0 by 7.7. Multicolored beaded bands in geometric patterns at top and bottom, buckskin fringe. Sioux tribe, XIX c. Gift of W. N. King, 1906.76.

236. **Shield,** rawhide with painted buckskin or antelope cover, diameter 51.0. Yellow and blue flying birds and upright bear (?), around edge are suspended hawk feathers on red trade cloth. Said to have been made by Chief Scarlet Thunder (Wadutawakinyan), Yankton-Sioux tribe, XIX c. Gift of General M. F. Force, 1894.1210.

237. **Dance Shield,** rawhide with painted buckskin cover, diameter 40.8. Painted blue stylized birds and geometric designs; from the cover hang long wide strips of red trade cloth with golden eagle wing feathers. Sioux tribe, XIX c. Gift of General M. F. Force, 1894.1228.

238. **Bow,** wood and sinew, length 111. Reverse curved, made from one piece of wood with sinew backing. From Plains, XIX c. Gift of Joseph H. Sharp, 1905.365.

239. **Bow,** ashwood and sinew, length 111.0. Simple curve of wood is sinew-backed with ends encased in gut. Sioux tribe, XIX c. Gift of General M. F. Force, 1894.1246.

240. **Bow,** osage orange wood, length 125.0., simple curve. Cheyenne tribe, Wyoming, XIX c. Gift of General M. F. Force, 1894.1037.

241. **Mounted Warrior's Club,** quartzite and leather, length 79.0. Blue-painted rawhide covers the handle and secures the egg-shaped stone head. Sioux tribe, Upper Missouri River area, XIX c. Gift of General M. F. Force, 1894.259.

242. **War Club or Battle Ax,** wood with iron knife blades, length 116.0. The brass-studded handle has three blades set into one side near the end with a hair braid (scalp lock?) at the tip. Sioux tribe, XIX c. Gift of General M. F. Force, 1894.1082.

243. **War Club,** wood, leather and stone, length 58.0, horsehair plume 68.0 long. From Plains, XIX c. X-1975.28.

244. **Parfleche,** painted rawhide, 33.2 by 58.5. Geometric design in blue, green, red and yellow. Sioux tribe, XIX c. Gift of Mrs. W. O. Owen, 1938.10629.

*245. **Baby Carrier,** beaded buckskin on wooden board, brass studs, length 108.0. The V-shaped board supports a wrap entirely covered with lazy-stitch beadwork, predominantly white with multicolored geometric design. From Northern Plains, Cheyenne or Sioux tribe, XX (?) c. Gift of Mrs. Philip Wyman, 1956.242.

*246. **Baby Wrap,** quilled and beaded elkskin and trade cloth, length 104.0. Top has floral quillwork with beaded edging, red cloth bottom bound in calico. Sioux tribe, Dakota, XIX c. Gift of General M. F. Force, 1894.1215.

247. **Baby Wrap,** buckskin with quill and beadwork, length 73.0. Top has vertical stripes of red quillwork with remnants of feathers; front edges beaded. Sioux tribe, XIX c. Gift of W. N. King, 1906.74.

248. **Birth Charm,** plummet-shaped, beaded buckskin, 10.3 by 5.2. Lozenges of yellow, green and blue beads solidly cover the surface, buckskin handle. Cheyenne tribe, Wyoming, XIX c. Gift of General M. F. Force, 1894.103.

249. **Birth Charm,** tortoise-shaped, beaded buckskin, tin cone pendants, 11.5 by 6.5. Blue and yellow beads cover one side. Cheyenne tribe, Wyoming, XIX c. Gift of General M. F. Force, 1894.102.

250. **Drum,** painted leather and wood, diameter 36.5, depth 5.0. **Drumstick,** wood covered with buckskin, quillwork head, length 43.0. From Plains, possibly Sioux tribe, XIX c. Gift of Mrs. O. E. Hilmer, 1973.546a, b.

251. **Rattle,** beaded leather-covered stick, deer's "dew claws" and horsehair, length 39.5. From Plains, possibly Sioux tribe, XIX c. Gift of Mrs. O. E. Hilmer, 1973.547.

252. **Dice (?) Basket,** willow, height 5.8, diameter 16.7, coiled construction, braided edge. From Fort Buford on the Montana-North Dakota line, XIX c. Gift of General M. F. Force, 1894.149.

*253. **Spoon,** cattle horn, molded and cut with the tip of the handle turned back and slightly carved to suggest an animal head, dyed porcupine quill around handle, length 24.3. From Dakota tribe, XIX c. Gift of General M. F. Force, 1894.968.

254. **Spoon,** horn, probably of mountain goat, handle wrapped with dyed porcupine quills, length 17.0. Recorded as from Alaska, but probably of Plains origin. Gift of Lucien Wulsin, 1964.961.

255. **Ladle,** mountain sheep horn, length 38.8. From Fort Buford on the Montana-North Dakota line, XIX c. Gift of General M. F. Force, 1894.150.

256. **Pipe Stem,** wood wrapped with dyed porcupine quills on sinew, length 48.5. From the Northern Plains, XIX c. Gift of General M. F. Force, 1894.71.

257. **Pipe Stem,** wood wrapped with dyed porcupine quills, horsehair and ribbons, length 73.0. From the Northern Plains, XIX c. Gift of General M. F. Force, 1894.1230.

258. **Pipe Stem,** divided wood stem wrapped with bird quill on sinew, horsehair, fur, ribbon, brass nails, length 68.5. Blackfeet tribe, Alberta, Canada, XIX c. Gift of General M. F. Force, 1894.1207.

259. **Pipe,** red pipestone, probably Catlinite, length 16.5. Tomahawk shape engraved with animal and plant forms. Tribal origin unknown, but possible Eastern Plains, XIX c. Gift of the Estate of Nettleton Neff, 1940.1214.

260. **Pipe,** red pipestone, probably Catlinite, with lead inlay, length 16.5, tomahawk shape. Tribal origin unknown, but probably Eastern Plains, XIX c. Gift of the Estate of Nettleton Neff, 1940.1209.

261. **Pipe,** red pipestone, probably Catlinite, length 14.0. From Fort Buford on the Montana-North Dakota line, XIX c. Gift of General M. F. Force, 1894.143.

262. **Feather Stick,** wood with feathers, length 72.5. A cluster of dyed red feathers at one end, use unknown, possibly for a secret society. From Plains area, XIX c. Gift of General M. F. Force, 1894.261.

The Great Basin

*263. **Winnowing Tray,** willow and redbud, 57.3 by 55.4. Twined construction with brown band across wide side, twig whipped on edge. Mono tribe, Yosemite Valley, XIX c. Gift of James W. Bullock, 1907.135.

264. **Basket-Hat,** cone-shaped, sumac with mud color, height 17.5, diameter 22. Twill twined construction with narrow horizontal bands of mud-dyed sumac. Paiute tribe, Utah, XIX c. Gift of United States National Museum, 1889.52.

265. **Basket,** for gathering seeds and insects, cone-shaped, sumac twigs, height 34.0, diameter 30.5. Twill-twined with heavy twigs and bent warps whipped down with splints around rim. Gosiute tribe, Deep Creek, Utah, XIX c., collected by H. C. Yarrow, 1884. Gift of United States National Museum, 1889.53.

266. **Harvesting Wand or Seed Beater,** sumac twigs, 53.3 by 56.0 including rigid handle. Coarse twined construction with twigs converging into handle, handle and rim whipped with splits and thongs. Gosiute tribe, Deep Creek, Utah, XIX c., collected by H. C. Yarrow, 1884. Gift of United States National Museum, 1889.56.

*267. **Basket,** for gathering and carrying seeds, cone-shaped, sumac, height 56.0, diameter 53.5. Twined construction with thick wood splint bound around rim, leather sling. Paiute tribe, Utah, XIX c., collected by J. W. Powell, 1885. Gift of United States National Museum, 1889.58.

268. **Fanning or Roasting Tray,** for separating seed from chaff and roasting seeds, sumac, 44.0 by 48.5. Twined construction of tans and browns, a rim formed by lashing on a twig. Paiute tribe, Utah, XIX c., collected by J. W. Powell, 1874. Gift of United States National Museum, 1889.54.

269. **Fanning Tray,** sumac twigs, 52.2 by 39.6. Openwork twined construction with two twigs whipped on the rim. Ute tribe, Utah, XIX c., collected by W. H. Havenor, 1885. Gift of United States National Museum, 1889.57.

270. **Basket,** willow and redbud, height 23.0, diameter 43.3. Coiled construction with "four-pointed star" geometric pattern. Washo tribe, Nevada, XIX c. Gift of James W. Bullock, 1907.126.

85

271. **Berry Basket,** willow splints, redbud and devil's claw, height 11.6, diameter 21.0. Coiled construction, geometric pattern of V's. Washo tribe, Nevada, XIX c. Gift of James W. Bullock, 1907-160.

272. **Baby Carrier,** sumac (?) twigs, 61.0 by 18.0. A "Y" stick frame with sharp base to hold cradle upright in ground, crossed with twigs and cord, twig canopy has loop of beads along edge. Paiute tribe, Utah, XIX c. Gift of Mrs. Erasmus Gest, 1896.144.

273. **Bow Case and Quiver,** mountain lion fur and trade cloth, length of quiver 63.7, of bowcase 99.5. Outside of quiver and inside of bowcase is fur, with long flap lined with red cloth and fringe. Ute tribe, XIX c. Gift of General M. F. Force, 1894.72, .73.

The Plateau

274. **Bag,** corn husk fibers with wool yarn, 29.4 by 28.0. Twined fibers with false embroidery of multicolored wool in geometric and animal forms. Source unknown, but style of Nez Perce tribe, XIX c. Gift of Mrs. C. L. Harrison, 1942.80.

275. **Bag,** corn husk fibers with wool yarn, 30.6 by 28.2. Twined fibers with false embroidery of multicolored wool in geometric stripes. Source unknown, but style of Nez Perce tribe, XIX c. Gift of Mr. and Mrs. Paul T. Ellsworth, 1941.246.

276. **Bag,** corn husk fibers with wool yarn, 28.2 by 25.0. Twined fibers with false embroidery of multicolored wool in geometric design. Source unknown, but style of Nez Perce tribe, XIX c. Gift of William N. King, 1906.73.

277. **Carrier Bag,** hemp with corn husks, 62.5 by 48.5. Twined weave of hemp base with false embroided pattern, thong drawstring at top. Source unknown, but style of Nez Perce tribe, XIX c. Gift of Mrs. H. S. Fechheimer, 1938.10619.

278. **Panel-Belt,** commercial leather with beadwork and nailheads, width 4.0. Areas of studded brass nailheads alternate with areas of beadwork. From Northern Plains or Plateau area, XIX-XX c. Gift of Amelia Elizabeth White, 1937.554.

279. **Moccasins,** buckskin with beads, length 25.0. On the front is a stylized floral pattern made up of seed, faceted and double-coated beads; the tongue is in one piece with moccasin. Source unknown, but style of Plateau area, possible Nez Perce or Shoshone tribe, XIX c. Gift of General M. F. Force, 1894.1223-1224.

280. **Moccasins,** buckskin with beads, length 27.5. A stylized floral pattern of plain and double-coated seed beads is on the front. Source unknown, but style of Plateau area, possibly Nez Perce tribe, XIX c. ? X-1975.33 a, b.

Eastern Woodlands

*281. **Basket-Tray,** split cane, height 5.0 by 17.5, square, rounded base, square top. Plaited double weave with dark orange and brown striped and geometric bands. Attakapa tribe, Louisiana, XIX c. Gift of Mrs. H. S. Fechheimer, 1938.10620.

282. **Basket,** split cane, height 5.5, diameter 9.0, square base, round top. Plaited double weave with orange and brown diagonal pattern. Attakapa tribe, Louisiana, XIX c. Gift of Estate of William Watts Taylor, 1913.718.

283. **Basket,** split cane, height 15.0, diameter 22.7, square base, round top. Plaited diaper twill pattern in dark brown and yellow, rigid handle of wrapped splints. Choctaw tribe, Louisiana, XIX c., collected by V. A. Hattier, 1885. Gift of United States National Museum, 1889.60.

284. **Basket,** cone-shaped "elbow" style, split cane, 36.0 by 37.0. Plaited diagonal weave with orange and brown geometric pattern, rigid handle. Choctaw tribe, Louisiana, XIX c. Gift of William N. King, 1906.154.

285. **Basket-Tray,** split cane, height 5.0 by 22.7, square. Plaited double-weave with brown, red and yellow pattern. Chitimacha tribe, Louisiana, XX c. Gift of Estate of William Watts Taylor, 1913.748.

286. **Basket, Gift-Style,** with pointed base to imitate a heart which Indians thought should accompany every gift, split cane, 8.0 by 10.0 by 5.0. Plaited in twill pattern of dark orange and yellow. Chitimacha tribe, Louisiana, XIX c., collected by C. E. Whitney, 1885. Gift of United States National Museum, 1889.59.

287. **Box with Lid,** rectangular, split cane, 8.8 by 14.0 by 10.0. Plaited double weave with brown and orange diagonals, rectangles and stripes. Chitimacha tribe, Louisiana, XX c. Gift of Estate of William Watts Taylor, 1913.740-741.

*288. **Box with Lid,** rectangular, split cane, 15.0 by 20.2 by 16.3. Plaited double weave with brown and orange diagonals, stripes and squares. Chitimacha, XX c. Gift of the Estate of William Watts Taylor, 1913.742-743.

289. **Box with Lid** (for thimbles?), split cane, height 7.0 by 3.8, square base, cylindrical body. Plaited double weave with brown and orange diamonds and squares. Chitimacha tribe, Louisiana, XX c. Gift of Estate of William Watts Taylor, 1913.736, .737.

290. **Elbow Pipe,** soapstone (?), height 4.2, length 5.8. Decorated with a three-dimensional figure of a man seated on the stem. This type of pipe was adopted by the Europeans from the Indians along with the use of tobacco, thus spreading eastward to Europe and from there around the world. Source unknown, but probably from the eastern seaboard, possibly North Carolina, early XVII c. Gift of Mrs. E. L. Flagg, 1882.964.

291. **Elbow Pipe,** soapstone (?), height 4.7, length 6.5. Decorated with a lizard (?) in relief on the bowl. Source unknown, but probably from the eastern seaboard, possibly North Carolina, early XVII c. 1938.5132.

292. **Elbow Pipe,** soapstone (?), height 4.5, length 7.0. Decorated with a three-dimensional animal crouching on the stem. Source unknown, but probably from the eastern seaboard, possibly North Carolina, early XVII c. 1938.5173.

293. **Shirt,** smoked moosehide, beads and trade cloth, length 78.0 from center neck to bottom. Navy cloth epaulettes and band around slashed neck opening have leather fringe, floral pattern in multicolored overlay beadwork. Probably Cree tribe, XIX c. X-1976.6.

294. **Pair of Moccasins,** leather, floss and beads, length 21.0. Pink leather with seams and cuff trimmed with embroidered floss and trade beads. Shawnee tribe, Ohio, said to have been owned by Governor Clark, 1829. Gift of Alice Dexter, 1913.661, .662.

295. **Pair of Moccasins,** buckskin and moosehair, length 19.0. Two types of leather with narrow band of colored hair. Probably Cree tribe, XIX c., X-1975.35.

296. **Pair of Child's Moccasins,** buckskin, cotton and quills, length 13.5. Flowered pattern of porcupine quills and bird feathers on front, cotton binding on cuff. Iroquois tribe, XIX c. Gift of Mrs. W. O. Owen, 1938.10634.

297. **Pair of Child's Moccasins,** buckskin and beads, length 16.0. Pattern of minute multicolored beads on front and cuff. From Eastern Woodlands, XIX c. Gift of Mrs. Sallie J. McCall, 1911.675.

298. **Pair of Leg Wraps (Garters),** beads, 38.0 by 7.0. Multicolored beads loom-woven in an abstract pattern. From Eastern Woodlands, XIX c. Gift of Lucien Wulsin, 1964.980-981.

299. **Man's Sash,** wool, 193.5 by 20.5 with 71.2

fringe. Diagonal finger-weaving in multicolor "lightning" pattern. Huron tribe, XIX c. Gift of Lucien Wulsin, 1907.281.

*300. **Man's Sash**, wool, 200 by 17.3 with 70.0 fringe. Diagonal finger-weaving in multicolor "lightning" pattern. Huron tribe, XIX c. Gift of Lucien Wulsin, 1907.282.

301. **Sash**, wool yarns, 82.0 by 21.0 with 66.0 fringe. Diagonal finger-weaving, multicolored pattern. Winnebago tribe, XX c. Gift of Milton G. Chandler, 1933.42.

302. **Shoulder Bag** for ceremonial occasions, cotton and beads, 46.0 by 42.0. Solidly covered with multicolored floral pattern of overlay beadwork, large beads and wool tassels at bottom, false pocket. Source unknown, but probably Woodlands, late XIX or early XX c. Gift of Mrs. O. E. Hilmer, 1973.548.

303. **Shoulder Bag**, velvet with beadwork, pouch 48.4 by 33.2. Pouch is solidly covered with overlay beadwork in multicolored floral pattern with black velvet band at top; 12.8 cm. wide shoulder bands same as pouch. Probably Ojibway tribe, XIX c., collected in North Dakota in 1888. Gift of Mrs. Dolly M. Ernst, 1942.86.

*304. **Shoulder Bag**, trade cloth with beadwork, pouch 39.7 by 28.0. Red cloth pouch has floral pattern of overlay beadwork at top, geometric pattern of loom-beadwork at bottom; 10.2 wide shoulder bands of loom-beading backed with cloth. Ojibway tribe, XIX c. Gift of Lucien Wulsin, 1964.984.

305. **Shoulder bag**, trade cloth with beadwork, pouch 38.3 by 25.5. Bottom part of maroon wool pouch is loom-beadwork in floral pattern with loom-beaded fringe and yarn tassels; 10.2 wide loom-beaded shoulder bands. From Central Woodlands area, XIX c. Gift of George W. Lewis for Annie K. Laws, 1928.231.

306. **Shoulder Bag**, trade cloth with beadwork, pouch 25.5 by 22.8. Red wool pouch is covered with floral pattern of overlay beadwork and edged with tin cones with yarn tassels; 12.2 wide shoulder bands are similar to pouch. Potawatomi tribe, XIX c. X-1975.32.

*307. **Bag**, buckskin with quillwork, 15.5 by 14.3. Multicolored quills in a geometric pattern, tin cones, trade, beads around edges. Shawnee tribe, XIX c. Gift of Annie and Catherine James, 1927.471.

308. **Bag**, buckskin, cotton and quillwork, 20.3 by 19.0. Navy resist-printed cotton has geometric border of quills edged with tin cones with red horsehair. Shawnee tribe, XIX c. Gift of Annie and Catherine James, 1927.472.

309. **Bag**, beaded velvet, 15.5 by 15.5. Black cotton velvet, envelope-style, with curving sides and tiny multicolored beads in outline and floral pattern. From Woodlands area, probably Iroquois tribe, XX c. Gift of Alice and Kate Neave, 1917.105.

310. **Bag**, beaded on velvet, 13.0 by 12.0. Brown cotton velvet, top flaps heavily covered with "padded" multicolored beadwork in floral pattern. Iroquois tribe, XIX c. Gift of Nelle Hosbrook, 1964.42.

311. **Bag**, beaded velvet, 16.5 by 17.0. Brown cotton velvet, flaps heavily covered with "padded" multicolored beadwork in floral pattern. Iroquois tribe, XIX c. Gift of Mrs. Howard D. Porter, 1964.917.

312. **Bag**, feathers, fur and beadwork, 46.0. by 18.5. Two vertical pockets, one covered with fur, one with neck feathers of male mallard duck, with separations of beadwork on red trade cloth. Probably from Woodlands, XIX c. Gift of Mrs. Howard D. Porter, 1964.915.

313. **Bag**, for storage and general utility, woolen fibers, 43.5 by 48.5. Finger-woven in twined weave with multicolor geometric pattern, buckskin thongs at top. Winnebago tribe, early XX c. Gift of Milton G. Chandler, 1933.39.

314. **Tubular Beads**, hard clam shell (quahog), each approximately 2 cm. long, alternating white and purple, wampum type. Source unknown, but probably from Eastern Woodlands. 1938.5036.

*315. **Snow Shoes**, wood, sinew and leather, 95.0 by 39.5. Bent wood frame is netted with sinew in a twined-cane technique, held to feet with leather thongs. From Sandpoint, Upper Canada, XIX c. Gift of Thomas Cleneay, 1887.20908.

316. **Box with Lid**, birchbark and porcupine quills, height 8.8, diameter 12.6, overall pattern of white quills, sweet grass around rim of lid. From Great Lakes, XX c. Gift of Estate of William Watts Taylor, 1913.790.

317. **Box with Lid**, birchbark and porcupine quills, height 7.6, diameter 12.6. Multicolored quills in floral pattern used to lace the edges. Huron tribe, XIX c. Gift of Mrs. S. Herbert Randall, 1911.1795.

The Southwest

*318. **Pitcher**, slip painted pottery, height 16.5. Zoned black geometric motifs on white slip. Said to come from Chaco Canyon, New Mexico, probably early Pueblo, about X-XII c. A.D. Gift of Amelia Elizabeth White, 1937.531.

319. **Bowl**, slip painted pottery, height about 10.5, diameter 20.4-20.8. Thin, dense body of pale clay probably covered with a thin white slip; black fret or labyrinth design inside; undecorated outside. Said to have been found in 1881 south of Walpi, Arizona, exposed by water erosion; probably early Pueblo, about X-XII c. A. D. Gift of General M. F. Force, 1894.296.

320. **Corrugated Coil Jar**, pottery, height 12.9. Said to come from New Mexico; probably early Pueblo, about X-XIII c. A.D. Gift of Amelia Elizabeth White, 1937.386.

321. **Storage or Cooking Vessel**, pottery, height 32.0, diameter 36.5. Said to come from New Mexico; probably early Pueblo. Gift of Amelia Elizabeth White, 1937.526.

*322. **Bowl**, slip painted pottery, height about 10.5, diameter 20.0-20.4. Inside, dark gray fringed triangles and spirals on white slip; outside, undecorated, unslipped grayish baked clay. Said to come from the vicinity of the Mesa Verde, southwestern Colorado; probably early Pueblo, about XII-XIII c. A.D. Gift of Mrs. J. H. Young, 1933.93.

323. **Pitcher or Handled Jar**, slip painted pottery, height about 17.0. Pale clay probably covered with a thin white slip; black fret decoration. Said to come from the upper Gila River area; probably Mogollon or early Pueblo, about XI-XV c. A.D. Gift of Amelia Elizabeth White, 1937.532.

324. **Bowl**, slip painted pottery, height 4.7-5.0, diameter 11.0-12.3. Inside, geometricized brown/black antelope on white slip; outside, unslipped baked clay. Said to have been found in the Gila River area; probably the Mimbres style of late Mogollon, about A.D. 1000-1500. Gift of Mrs. W. O. Owen, 1901.49.

*325. **Bowl**, slip painted pottery, height 9.5-10.5, diameter 20.8-22.5. Inside, white slipped with a brown fish in the center; brown/black banding below lip; outside, white slipped; "killed." Said to have come from the mountains near Fort Bayard, New Mexico; Mimbres style of late Mogollon, about XI-XV c. A.D. Gift of Mrs. W. O. Owen, 1901.48.

*326. **Storage Jar**, slip painted pottery, height about 30.0, diameter about 33.0. Globular body, short straight neck; covered with a white slip and decorated with black pigment that slightly beads up on the surface, in a pattern of hatched angular meanders and a series of "bird tracks" on the neck. Source unknown, but probably early Pueblo, XII-XIV c. A.D. X-1975.17.

*327. **Human Effigy Jar,** slip painted pottery, height 19.0. Red and black geometric decoration on polished buff ground. From Casas Grandes, Chihuahua, northern Mexico, Late Period, after A.D. 1300. Formerly collection of Mrs. B. P. Wagner, Sidney, Ohio. Museum purchase, 1929.227.

328. **Small Globular Jar,** slip painted pottery, height 10.5, diameter 15.0. Red and black geometrical decoration on polished buff ground. From Casas Grandes, Late Period. Formerly Wagner collection. Museum purchase, 1929.236.

329-335. **Child's Miniature Bowls and Jar,** pottery, height 2.0-5.0. From Casas Grandes. Formerly Wagner collection. Museum purchase, 1929.282-.287, .290.

336. **Bowl,** slip painted pottery, height 10.3, diameter 15.0. Red and black geometric decoration on polished buff ground. From Casas Grandes, Late Period. Formerly Wagner collection. Museum purchase, 1929.241.

337. **Biconical Jar,** slip painted pottery, height 19.5, diameter 22.0. Red and black geometric decoration on polished buff ground. Casas Grandes, Late Period. Formerly Wagner collection. Museum purchase, 1929.222.

338. **Jar pottery,** height 15.5, diameter 22.0. Dark red polished surface, possibly slipped, blackened above shoulder, blackened inside neck. From Casas Grandes. Formerly Wagner collection. Museum purchase, 1929-247.

339. **Bowl,** slip painted pottery, height 7.5, diameter 11.5. Red, black and white geometric decoration on polished buff ground. From Casas Grandes, Late Period. Formerly Wagner collection. Museum purchase, 1929.259.

340. **Jar,** slipped, polished and incised pottery, height 9.5, diameter 11.2. Lower half, polished orange ground; upper half, zoned zigzag and median line of dark red polished slip, incised hatching; double holes on opposite sides of rim. From Casas Grandes. Formerly Wagner collection. Museum purchase, 1929.255.

341. **Double-Gourd Bottle,** black slipped pottery, height 12.0. From Casas Grandes. Formerly Wagner collection. Museum purchase, 1929.273.

342. **Double-Gourd Bottle,** black slipped pottery, height 14.8. From Casas Grandes. Formerly Wagner collection. Museum purchase, 1929.272.

343. **Biconical Jar,** black slipped pottery, height 18.7, diameter 27.0. From Casas Grandes. Formerly Wagner collection. Museum purchase, 1929.277.

344. **Globular Jar,** black slipped pottery, height 13.0, diameter 15.0. Two pierced-lug handles. From Casas Grandes. Formerly Wagner collection. Museum purchase, 1929.276.

345. **Globular Jar,** red slipped pottery, height 9.7, diameter 13.0. Two pierced-lug handles. From Casas Grandes. Formerly Wagner collection. Museum purchase, 1929.257.

346. **Jar,** dark red slipped pottery, height 13.0, diameter 17.0 "killed." From Casas Grandes. Formerly Wagner collection. Museum purchase, 1929.249.

347. **Vertical Compound Vessel,** dark orange slipped pottery, height 11.0, diameter 13.0. Smoke-blackened, dark orange polished slip covers outside and part way down inside; lower half of jar is smooth, upper half is modeled to resemble corrugated coiled ware. From Casas Grandes. Formerly Wagner collection. Museum purchase, 1929.252.

348. **Bowl,** slip painted pottery, height 12.5, diameter 17.4. Black and orange geometrical motifs and crescents on white ground. From Acoma Pueblo, New Mexico, XIX c. Gift of the Women's Art Museum Association (received from the United States National Museum, Washington, D.C., in trade for Rookwood pottery), 1885.56.

349. **Water Jar,** slip painted pottery, height 27.0, diameter 30.0. Lozenges of black hatching and orange monochrome alternating with white; lowest zone orange; old repair of a crack by means of a leather thong. From Acoma Pueblo, XIX c. Gift of Amelia Elizabeth White, 1937.525.

350. **Canteen,** slip painted pottery, height 25.0, diameter 22.0. Orange and black geometric motifs on white ground. From Acoma Pueblo, XIX c. Gift of the Women's Art Museum Association (received from the United States National Museum in trade for Rookwood pottery), 1885.64.

*351. **Jar,** slip painted pottery, height 22.5, diameter 27.0. Black and red geometricized plant forms and meanders on white ground. From Acoma Pueblo, late XIX or early XX c. Gift of William N. King, 1906.61.

*352. **Jar,** slip painted pottery, height 23.0, diameter 23.5. Bird and geometric motifs in black and two reds on a white ground; red slip inside neck; two loop handles on opposite sides of shoulder. From Acoma Pueblo, XIX or early XX c. Gift of William N. King, 1906.62.

353. **Bowl,** slip painted pottery, height 14.0, diameter 25.3. Roughly hemispherical with slight constriction at lip; white slip inside and out; black geometric and geometricized plant motifs. From Acoma Pueblo, XIX c., collected by James Stevenson for the Bureau of Ethnology. Gift of the Women's Art Museum Association (received from the United States National Museum in trade for Rookwood pottery), 1885.57.

354. **Storage Jar,** slip painted pottery, height 27.3, diameter 29.1. White ground, black and red monochrome and hatched triangles, squares, crescents and checkerboards; underbody dark brown; rim-edge black; red band inside lip; thin-walled, dense body. Source unknown but probably Acoma Pueblo, XX c. Gift of Mrs. Powers, 1965.471.

355. **Jar,** slip painted pottery, height 22.9, diameter 27.1. White ground, black geometricized natural forms and zigzags; red slipped underbody and inside. Said to come from Cochiti Pueblo, New Mexico. Gift of Amelia Elizabeth White, 1937.516.

356. **Bird-Effigy Bottle,** slip painted pottery, height 22.0. Black linear and positive-negative decoration on light pinkish-tan slip; band of red slip below lowest framing lines; polished orange-buff underbody and base. Source unknown, but probably Cochiti Pueblo, New Mexico, XX c. X-1976.1.

*357. **Flattened Jar,** slip painted pottery, height 16.0, diameter 37.7. Yellow-orange ground, brown/black triangles, checkers and four geometricized birds. Source unknown, but style of the 1890's Hopi revival of the Sikyatki style. X-1975.18.

358. **Beaker,** slip painted pottery, height 16.0, diameter 8.7. Yellow-orange ground, brown and deep yellow geometric motifs. From the Hopi area of Arizona. Gift of Dr. Daniel Cook, 1943.925.

359. **Jar,** slip painted pottery, height 16.8, diameter 21.5. Orange-stained white ground; black finned spirals; dark orange slip inside and on underbody. From Moqui (Hopi) area, collected at a time when the Hopis were producing pottery in the style of Zuni, Bureau of Ethnology number 84670. Gift of the Women's Art Museum Association (received from the United States National Museum in trade for Rookwood pottery), 1885.55.

360. **Jar,** slip painted pottery, height 15.7, diameter 18.0. White ground, orange spots and plant forms, brown hatching and checkering; dark orange slip on underbody and inside lip; white slip inside body. Said to come from Isleta Pueblo, New Mexico, XIX or early XX c. Gift of William N. King, 1906.64.

361. **Bird Effigy Bottle,** slip painted pottery, height 20.7. Black outline drawings of water creatures and stars/flowers on white polished slip, with a fish in relief on the back of the bird's neck; orange-red below lowest double black framing lines. Said to come from Isleta Pueblo, New Mexico, but the style resembles that of Cochiti, XIX or early XX c. Gift of William N. King, 1906.65.

362. **Jar,** slip painted pottery, height 22.5, diameter 27.0. Red and black geometric and life forms on white slip; red slip inside neck; white slip inside body; red slipped underbody; marked offset from middle body to underbody. Said to come from Laguna Pueblo, New Mexico, XIX or early XX c. Gift of William N. King, 1906.59.

363. **Jar,** slip painted pottery, height 21.8, diameter 25.7. Red and black geometric and red and orange geometricized plant forms on white slip; red slip inside neck; white slip inside body. Said to come from Laguna Pueblo, XIX or early XX c. Gift of William N. King, 1906.60.

364. **Canteen,** slip painted pottery, height 19.5. Flattened sphere with single spout and two loop handles at sides and one at bottom; brown linked circles and spots on red-orange unslipped ground. From the Mojave area, Arizona, XIX c. Gift of Major George A. Glenn, 1887.79.

365. **Four-Spout Jar,** slip painted pottery, height 18.8. Blind spout in center rising to a human head surmounted by a handle with a three-strand necklace of black and white beads around the neck; brown zigzags and spots on red-orange unslipped ground. From the Mojave area, Arizona, XIX or early XX c. Gift of William N. King, 1906.68.

366. **Four-Spout Jar,** slip painted pottery, height 13.6. Handles rising from spouts form an X meeting in the center; brown lines and spots on red-orange unslipped ground. From Mojave area, Arizona, XIX or early XX c. Gift of William N. King, 1906.69.

*367. **Doll,** slip painted pottery and applied black hair, bead necklaces, calico skirt, height 17.0. The body is complete with arms and legs, medium buff unslipped paste decorated with red spots and geometric patterns and black vertical lines on the chin. From the Mojave area, Arizona or California, XIX or early XX c. Gift of Mrs. Charles Fleischmann, 1911.1678.

368. **Doll,** slip painted pottery with applied black hair, wool and vegetable fiber, height about 13.8. The figure has arms holding a bowl of eggs (?) but lacks legs; dark red unslipped pottery decorated with grayish white lines and red slip cross bars on the face and torso. From the Mojave area, Arizona, XIX or early XX c. Gift of Mrs. Charles Fleischmann, 1911.1681.

*369. **Ovoid Storage Jar,** black slipped pottery, height 53.6, diameter about 40.8. Exterior entirely covered with black polished slip, impressed bear-paw motif on shoulder. From Santa Clara Pueblo, New Mexico, XIX or early XX c. Gift of Amelia Elizabeth White, 1937.527.

370. **Storage Jar,** black slipped pottery, height 46.8, diameter 50.5. Globular shape, flat bottom; exterior black polished slip down to mid-zone, brown/black polished body clay from there down. Said to come from Santa Clara Pueblo, but use of the two polished blacks was more popular in San Juan Pueblo nearby, XIX or early XX c. Gift of Amelia Elizabeth White, 1937.377.

371. **Bird-Effigy Bottle,** black slipped pottery, height 14.2. From Santa Clara Pueblo, XIX c. Gift of Mrs. Larz Anderson through the Women's Art Museum Association, 1881.4.

372. **Double-Spout Wedding Vessel,** black slipped pottery, height 29.5. Step and crescent motifs impressed into shoulder. From Santa Clara Pueblo, probably XX c. Gift of Amelia Elizabeth White, 1937.530.

373. **Jar,** black slipped pottery, height 13.8, diameter 18.7. Scalloped lip, concave base. From Santa Clara Pueblo, XIX c., collected by James Stevenson. Gift of the Women's Art Museum Association (received from the United States National Museum in trade for Rookwood pottery), 1885.59.

374. **Jar,** black slipped pottery, height 16.0, diameter 19.8. Source unknown, but the meander impressed on the shoulder of this jar marks it as probably coming from Santa Clara Pueblo although the black slipped upper body with polished black unslipped underbody was more popular in San Juan Pueblo, XIX c. Gift of General M. F. Force, 1894.324.

375. **Storage Jar,** black slipped pottery, height 36.5, diameter 51.0. Polished black slipped upper body; polished black unslipped underbody. Source unknown, but probably San Juan Pueblo, New Mexico. Gift of Amelia Elizabeth White, 1937.529.

*376. **Bread Bowl,** slip painted pottery, height 25.9, diameter 39.4. Black and white geometricized leaf and checkers; red slip band about 5.0 wide below lowest framing lines; unslipped brick-red underbody; black rim; interior slipped red-orange; "killed." From Santo Domingo Pueblo, New Mexico, XIX or early XX c. Gift of Amelia Elizabeth White, 1937.385.

377. **Bowl,** slip painted pottery, height 16.0, diameter 25.0 Black geometricized plant motifs on white polished slip; red-orange slip on underbody and interior; black rim. From Santo Domingo Pueblo, New Mexico, probably XX c. Gift of Amelia Elizabeth White, 1937.378.

378. **Jar,** slip painted pottery, height 26.4, diameter 27.4. Black stylized plant forms on white polished slip; red-orange slip inside neck and on underbody; black rim. From Santo Domingo Pueblo, New Mexico, said to be XIX c. Gift of Amelia Elizabeth White, 1937.380.

379. **Bread Bowl,** slip painted pottery, height 24.0, diameter 45.6. Black and white lozenges and black leaf forms on white polished slip; red slip on underbody but not base; white slip inside; black rim. From Santo Domingo Pueblo, New Mexico, probably XX c. Gift of Amelia Elizabeth White, 1937.513.

380. **Black on Black Jar** by Maria Martinez, born about 1886, slip painted pottery, height 9.9, diameter 15.7. Decorated with matte and polished triangles on shoulder, probably by her husband Julian who decorated most of her pottery until he died in 1943. Signed on bottom: "Marie" incised before firing; "Martinez" engraved after firing. From San Ildefonso Pueblo, New Mexico, made between approximately 1923 and 1943. Gift of Dr. Daniel Cook, 1943.924.

*381. **Black on Black Plate** by Maria Martinez, born about 1886, slip painted pottery, diameter 37.7. Decorated with eagle feathers radiating from a circle in the center, probably by Maria's husband Julian. Signed on the bottom: "Marie" incised before firing. From San Ildefonso Pueblo, New Mexico, made between approximately 1923 and 1943. Gift of Mrs. Lucien Wulsin, 1966.502.

382. **Black on Black Plate** by Maria and Santana Martinez, slip painted pottery, diameter 37.2. Decorated with eagle feathers radiating from the center, by Maria's daughter-in-law Santana who decorated some of Maria's pottery after Julian's death in 1943. Signed on the bottom: "Marie & Santana" incised before firing. From San Ildefonso Pueblo, New Mexico, probably between 1943 and 1948. Gift of Mrs. Howard Wurlitzer, 1948.174.

383. **Pair of Candlesticks** by Maria and Santana Martinez, black slipped pottery, height 8.8. Signed on bottom: "Marie & Santana" incised before firing. From San Ildefonso Pueblo, New Mexico. Gift of Mrs. Lucien Wulsin, 1966.500.

384. **Black on Black Jar** by Santana Martinez, slip painted pottery, height 14.2, diameter 16.6. Dec-

orated with matte and polished stepped spirals. Signed on bottom: "Santana" incised before firing. From San Ildefonso Pueblo, New Mexico, made before 1937. Gift of Amelia Elizabeth White, 1937.518.

385. **Male Figure,** micaceous pottery, height 18.8. Seated naked figure, purplish red spots painted chiefly on head, probably after firing; black firing clouds on back and back of head; mouth open as if singing; topknot. Source unknown, but possibly from Tesuque Pueblo, New Mexico. X-1972.40.

386. **Storage Jar,** slip painted pottery, height 23.0, diameter 27.0. Red flowers and black leaves on cream slip; underbody red slipped; concave base; inside unslipped. Said to come from Zia Pueblo, New Mexico, XIX or early XX c. Gift of Amelia Elizabeth White, 1937.522.

387. **Storage Jar,** slip painted pottery, height 46.9, diameter 53.5. Red and black rosettes, hatched geometric motifs, two zones of deer or elk showing heart line, one zone of long-tailed birds, on a white polished slip; black rim; unpolished white slip inside. From Zuni Pueblo, New Mexico, probably XX c. Gift of Dr. Daniel Cook, 1943.930.

388. **Water Jar,** slip painted pottery, height 33.0, diameter 35.2. Black steps, circles, rosettes, etc., on polished white slip; black underbody; black band inside neck, white inside rest of body; black rim, concave base. From Zuni Pueblo, New Mexico, probably XX c. Gift of Amelia Elizabeth White, 1937.383.

389. **Storage Jar,** slip painted pottery, height 23.3, diameter 31.5. Black and red solid and hatched triangles, frets, spirals and circles on white polished slip. From Zuni Pueblo, probably XX c. Gift of Amelia Elizabeth White, 1937.524.

390. **Food Bowl,** slip painted pottery, height 17.2, diameter 37.4. Exterior has black and red steps on a cream polished slip; underbody brown slip. Interior has black and red center circle, two radiating finned spirals and triangles with a hook at one end and a spiral at the other in clusters, on white slip. From Zuni Pueblo, New Mexico, XIX c., collected by James Stevenson, Bureau of Ethnology number 111922. Gift of the Women's Art Museum Association (received from the United States National Museum in trade for Rookwood pottery), 1885.70.

391. **Jar,** slip painted pottery, height 23.4, diameter 29.7. Black and brown wasps, frog, tadpoles, dragonflies on white polished slip; white slip inside; red-brown slipped underbody. Inscribed just above underbody, "Ceremonial Bowl made by Lena Zuni—Zuni N. Mex. D. Cook 1933." Gift of Dr. Daniel Cook, 1943.931.

392. **Storage Jar,** slip painted pottery, height 24.5, diameter 30.9. Black steps on red polished slip above black and red step and plant motifs on white polished slip; flat base; interior unslipped; old crack tied with thongs, neck reinforced with string. From Zuni Pueblo, probably XIX c. Gift of Amelia Elizabeth White, 1937.381.

393. **Bowl,** slip painted pottery, height 11.5, diameter 32.0. Exterior, step motifs in two shades of brown on white slip; interior, two browns on white slip, four finned spirals radiating from center circle. From Zuni Pueblo, New Mexico, XIX c., collected by James Stevenson, Bureau of Ethnology number illegible. Gift of the Women's Art Museum Association (received from United States National Museum in trade for Rookwood pottery), 1885.71.

*394. **Storage Jar,** slip painted pottery, height 29.2, diameter 34.7. On a white polished slip, three zones of black deer with red heart lines, zone of long-tailed birds, alternately black and red; black underbody. From Zuni Pueblo, New Mexico, XIX c., collected by James Stevenson, Bureau of Ethnology number 111785. Gift of the Women's Art Museum Association (received from United States National Museum in trade for Rookwood pottery), 1885.48.

395. **Handled Bowl,** slip painted pottery, height 15.2, diameter 24.6. Stepped rim rising to four peaks; single handle; decorated inside with black and red dragonflies on white polished slip; outside with black horned toads on white slip. From Zuni Pueblo, New Mexico, XIX c., collected by James Stevenson. Gift of the Women's Art Museum Association (received from United States National Museum in trade for Rookwood pottery), 1885.76.

396. **Bowl,** slip painted pottery, height 8.7, diameter 19.4. Stepped rim, pinkish cream slip inside and out; black tadpoles on outside; horned toad and dragonflies inside. From Zuni Pueblo, New Mexico, XIX c. Gift of Women's Art Museum Association (received from United States National Museum in trade for Rookwood pottery), 1885.73.

397. **Owl Effigy with Mouse in its Beak,** slip painted pottery, height 17.7. Feathers, eyes and other details drawn in brown and orange on a white polished slip; the mouse is a separate piece of pottery, loose in the beak; base rounded like a jar. Inscribed: "Zuni Tribe New Mexico 1933 Daniel Cook." Gift of Dr. Daniel Cook. 1943.915.

398. **Bird Effigy Bottle,** slip painted pottery, height 23.9. Black stars/flowers, serpent, horned creatures, plants, on polished orange slip showing minute, widely scattered flecks of mica (?); white band and red band at beginning of underbody; ochre-slipped base; eyes, tail and stub wings in relief; beak open to the interior, small round made hole in the back of the neck. Said to have come from Zuni Pueblo, New Mexico, probably XX c., but style suggests Cochiti origin. Gift of Mary Hanna, 1925.582.

399. **Jar,** slip painted pottery, height 15.3, diameter 20.1. Black and red hatched swastikas and other geometrical motifs on polished white slip; underbody and base orange slipped; inside of neck black slipped; inside of body white slipped. From Zuni Pueblo, New Mexico, XIX c. Gift of the Women's Art Museum Association (received from the United States National Museum in trade for Rookwood pottery), 1885.53.

400. **Masked Dancers** by Fred Kabotie (Nakayoma), born 1900 (?), Hopi tribe, one of the pioneers of twentieth-century Pueblo painting, gouache on paper, height 35.5, width 45.5. The dancers are wearing characteristic Hopi embroidered sashes and kilts like No. 433 and 437. Gift of Amelia Elizabeth White, 1937.610.

401. **Buffalo Dance** by Tonita Peña (Quah Ah), 1895-1949, native of San Ildefonso Pueblo, New Mexico, later moved to Cochiti Pueblo; member of a family known for their pottery; the only woman painter of her generation and one of the pioneers of the twentieth-century Pueblo painting movement. Gouache on paper, height 45.5, width 60.7. Gift of Amelia Elizabeth White, 1937.389.

402. **Eagle Dancers** by Tonita Peña (Quah Ah), 1895-1949, gouache on paper, height 31.0, width 37.7. Gift of Amelia Elizabeth White, 1937.614.

403. **The Drummer** by Tonita Peña (Quah Ah), 1895-1949, gouache on paper, height 35.9, width 20.0. Gift of Amelia Elizabeth White, 1937.613.

404. **Corn Dance** by Tonita Peña (Quah Ah), 1895-1949, gouache on paper, height 56.0, width 71.3. Gift of Amelia Elizabeth White, 1937.615.

405. **Ceremonial Dance** by Abel Sanchez (Oqua Pi), about 1900-1971, San Ildefonso Pueblo, New Mexico, gouache on cardboard, height 30.4, width 55.9. Gift of Amelia Elizabeth White, 1937.619.

406. **Dog Dancers** by Abel Sanchez (Oqua Pi), about 1900-1971, gouache on cardboard, height 35.7, width 56.0. Gift of Amelia Elizabeth White, 1937.388.

407. **Mounted Warrior** by Richard Martinez (Opa Mu Nu), born 1904, San Ildefonso Pueblo, New Mexico, gouache on paper, height 28.0, width 35.5. Gift of Amelia Elizabeth White, 1937.611.

*408. **Deer Dance** by Julian Martinez (Pocano), 1897-1943, San Ildefonso Pueblo, New Mexico; husband of Maria Martinez and decorator of her pottery; gouache on paper, height 35.5, width 55.5. Gift of Amelia Elizabeth White, 1937.387.

409. **Buffalo Dancers** by Alfonso Roybal (Awa Tsireh), about 1895-1955, San Ildefonso Pueblo, New Mexico, gouache on cardboard, height 29.0, width 36.2. Gift of Amelia Elizabeth White, 1937.616.

410. **Navajo Dancer** by Alfonso Roybal (Awa Tsireh), about 1895-1955, gouache on paper, height 27.9, width 18.0. Gift of Dr. Robert J. M. Horton, 1969.4.

411. **Mounted Warrior** by Alfonso Roybal (Awa Tsireh), about 1895-1955, gouache on paper, height 23.0, width 15.4. Gift of Amelia Elizabeth White, 1937.618.

412. **Eagle Dancers** by Alfonso Roybal (Awa Tsireh), about 1895-1955, gouache on paper, height 28.5, width 36.3. Gift of Amelia Elizabeth White, 1937.617.

413. **Comanche Dance** by Thomas Vigil (Pan Yo Pin), about 1889-1960, Tesuque Pueblo, New Mexico, gouache on paper, height 28.0, width 30.5. Gift of Amelia Elizabeth White, 1937.612.

414. **Corn Dance Procession** by Velino Shije Herrera (Ma Pe Wi), born 1902, Zia Pueblo, New Mexico, gouache on paper, height 45.7, width 60.7. Gift of Amelia Elizabeth White, 1937.390.

*415. **Double-Face Blanket,** wool, 190.5 by 131.5. Obverse red ground with natural white, navy and gold jagged diamonds; reverse striped red, purple, orange, navy, natural white, green; warp-fringe at one end. Navajo tribe, 1885-1900. Gift of Mrs. C. Gordon Neff, 1937.373.

*416. **Chief's Blanket,** wool, 137.0 by 168.0. Firmly packed weft, stripes of brown-black and natural white with center and edge stripes of navy, brown and red-violet stripes and stepped diamonds. Navajo tribe, early third phase style, 1870-80. Has tag indicating it was in Fred Harvey collection. Gift of Edward Foote Hinkle, 1944.115.

417. **Rug,** in style of **Chief's Blanket,** third phase, wool, 164.0 by 229.0. Narrow stripes of brown-black and natural white with center and edge stripes of narrow red and brown stripes with stepped diamonds. Navajo tribe, probably 1920-30. Gift of Amelia Elizabeth White, 1937.571.

418. **Rug,** in style of **Chief's Blanket,** third phase, wool, 117.0 by 178.2. Firmly packed weft; stripes of black and natural white with center and edge stripes of red and dark grey stripes with stepped diamonds. Navajo tribe, probably 1920-30. Gift of Amelia Elizabeth White, 1937.573.

419. **Rug,** in style of **Chief's Blanket,** transitional style, cotton warp, analine dyed wool weft, 164 by 214. Stripes of brown-black and natural white with center stripes of red, white and brown diamonds, and edge stripes of red, yellow and black-brown diamonds. Navajo tribe, 1890-1910. Gift of Ralph R. Caldwell, 1937-623.

420. **Blanket,** cotton warp, Germantown (?) wool, 209.0 by 155.0. "Eye dazzler" pattern of zigzagged diamonds in natural white, red, navy, browns and gold. Navajo tribe, about 1890. Bequest of Ruth H. Harrison, 1940.706.

421. **Blanket,** wool, 177.0 by 132.0. Predominately red with horizontal zigzags of navy, natural white, green, yellow, and pink. Navajo tribe, XX c. Gift of Amelia Elizabeth White, 1937.572.

422. **Blanket,** multi-purpose, wool, 214.0 by 130.0. Stripes of varied width of natural white, brown and yellow, in a classic Pueblo design; done by Navajo tribe, late XIX or early XX c. Gift of Amelia Elizabeth White, 1937.565.

423. **Blanket** or **Rug,** multi-purpose, wool, 184.0 by 128.0. Loosely spun and woven to give a soft hand; natural white and narrow red with black stripes. Navajo tribe, late XIX c. Gift of Amelia Elizabeth White, 1937.569.

424. **Rug,** multi-purpose, cotton warp, wool weft, 189.0 by 122.0. Loosely spun and woven to give a soft hand; lengthwise chevrons of red, natural white, brown-black, and orange, forming diamonds in center. Navajo tribe, XX c. Gift of Amelia Elizabeth White, 1937.566.

425. **Rug,** wool, 307.0 by 142.0. Classic style with blue-black ground, diagonals and diamonds of natural white and red. Navajo tribe, XX c. Gift of Amelia Elizabeth White, 1937.568.

426. **Rug,** wool, 216.0 by 134.0. "Eye dazzler" pattern of triangles and diamonds in orange-brown, yellow and brown-black. Navajo tribe, 1880-1890. Gift of Amelia Elizabeth White, 1937.394.

427. **Rug,** Germantown wool, 212.0 by 149.0. Finely woven red ground with narrow black and natural white "crosses" and stepped diamonds, probably a revival of an old design. Navajo tribe, 1900-1920. Bequest of Ruth Harrison, 1940.704.

428. **Saddle Blanket,** single, wool, 39.0 by 90.0. Diagonal twill woven of natural brown-black wools with red "lightning" in each corner. Navajo tribe, late XIX or early XX c. Gift of Amelia Elizabeth White, 1937.564.

429. **Saddle Blanket,** cotton warp, Germantown wool, 135.0 by 86.0. Finely woven red ground with navy and natural white overlapping frets; remnants of fringe at ends. Navajo tribe, late XIX or early XX c. Gift of Amelia Elizabeth White, 1937.567.

430. **Woman's Robe,** two woolen blankets, each 117.0 by 68.7. Black with woven red and black bands near top and bottom, sewn together across shoulders and down the sides. Navajo tribe, probably XX c. Gift of Amelia Elizabeth White, 1937-563.

431. **Sash,** wool warp, cotton string weft, 213.5 by 12.6 plus 30.6 self fringe at each end. Warp-woven on a belt loom; red flecked with white and narrow green stripes. Navajo tribe, XX c. Gift of Amelia Elizabeth White, 1937.544.

432. **Sash,** wool warp, cotton string weft, 172.5 by 9.5 plus 43.3 self fringe at each end. Warp-woven on a belt loom in red with white diamond pattern and narrow green stripes; fringe has shells, beads and metal attached. Navajo tribe, late XIX c. (?) Gift of Miss Jennette Reid Tandy, 1942.105.

433. **Dance Sash,** cotton string, wool yarn, 218.0 by 24.5 plus 14.0 fringe at each end. Woven of cotton with brocaded wool design of red, black, dark green and navy at each end. From Pueblo area, XX c. Gift of Mrs. Russell Wilson, 1948.197.

434. **Sash,** wool, 229.5 by 8.8 plus 25.5 self fringe at each end. Warp-woven on a belt loom with a central red stripe edged with black and green. From Hopi area, Arizona, XX c. Gift of Amelia Elizabeth White, 1937.542.

435. **Sash,** wool, 213.5 by 10.1 plus 20.4 self fringe at each end. Warp-woven on a belt loom in striped pattern of red, green and black. From Hopi area, Arizona, XX c. Gift of Mrs. Russell Wilson, 1948.198.

436. **Sash,** wool warp, cotton string weft, 377.5 by 10.1 plus 40.7 self fringe at each end. Warp-woven on a belt loom in red flecked with white and narrow green stripes. Navajo tribe, XX c. Gift of Amelia Elizabeth White, 1937.543.

437. **Kilt,** cotton and wool yarn, 128.5 by 66.3. Woven of cotton and wool with embroidered wool design of red, black, dark green and navy on the sides. From Pueblo area, XX c. Gift of Mrs. Russell Wilson, 1948.199.

*438. **Shirt,** cotton string, wool yarn, 76.0 from center neck to bottom. Woven of cotton and wool with wide band of brocaded wool design in red, black, dark green and navy; open sides. From Pueblo area, XX c. Gift of Mrs. Russell Wilson, 1948.200.

439. **Moccasins,** painted buckskin and rawhide, length 25.0. Streaks of yellow and blue color on high back and sides fastened with thong; rawhide upturned soles. From Eastern Pueblo area or Apache tribe, early XX (?) c. Gift of W. J. Baer, 1921.259, .260.

440. **Belt,** silver and leather, length 108.0. Seven silver "conchas" and buckle with stamped designs strung on a strip of commercial leather 2.2 wide. Navajo tribe, late XIX or early XX c. Gift of Amelia Elizabeth White, 1937.607.

*441. **Belt,** silver and leather, length 100.0. Seven silver "conchas" and buckle with stamped designs strung on a narrow commercial leather band backed with scalloped leather. Navajo tribe, early XX c. Gift of Amelia Elizabeth White, 1937.608.

442. **Conical Pendants,** shell. From Casas Grandes, about XIV c. Formerly Wagner collection. Museum purchase 1929.300.

443. **Beads,** mixed shells, shell disks and two small turquoise nuggets. From Casas Grandes, about XIV c. Formerly Wagner collection. Museum purchase, 1929.295.

444. **Beads,** mixed shells, white shell disks, violet shell disks, white shell fiddle-shaped beads, stone pendant in the form of a bird. From Casas Grandes, about XIV c. Formerly Wagner collection. Museum purchase, 1929.296, .311.

445. **Beads,** shell disks, five small bones, turquoise disk. From Casas Grandes, about XIV c. Formerly Wagner collection. Museum purchase, 1929.302.

446. **Tubular Beads,** shell. From Casas Grandes, about XIV c. Formerly Wagner collection. Museum purchase, 1929.303, .304.

*447. **Necklace,** shell, turquoise, jet (?) and bone, length 6.6. Shell disks, bone teardrop-shaped pendants, each overlaid with turquoise bits and a black band. From Pueblo area, probably Zuni, late XIX or early XX c. Gift of Amelia Elizabeth White, 1937.578.

448. **Necklace,** shell, turquoise and coral, length 62.0. Two strands of shell disks, randomly strung with irregular, flat turquoise nuggets and slices of coral. From Pueblo area, XIX c. Gift of Amelia Elizabeth White, 1937.580.

449. **Necklace,** shell and turquoise, length 7.0. Three strands of shell disks randomly strung with larger irregular turquoise nuggets and shell. From Pueblo area, XIX c. Gift of Amelia Elizabeth White, 1937.575.

450. **Necklace,** shells, turquoise and stones, length 75.0. Strand of shell disks strung with a large matrix turquoise pendant and various types of shells, stones and turquoises. From Pueblo area, XIX c. Gift of Amelia Elizabeth White, 1937.576.

451. **Necklace,** turquoise, length 53.0. Smooth turquoise disks of graduated size, European fastening. From Pueblo area, XX c. Gift of Amelia Elizabeth White, 1937.583.

452. **Necklace,** coral, turquoise and brass beads, length 72.0. Seven strands of smooth, tubular coral beads interspersed with turquoise nuggets and brass beads. From Pueblo area, XIX c. Gift of Amelia Elizabeth White, 1937. 582.

453. **Necklace,** shell and turquoise, length 60.0. Shell disks randomly strung with turquoise nuggets of varied sizes and shapes. **Jocla** (ear loops), graduated turquoise disks and four red beads. The *jocla* are transferred from the ears to the necklace upon marriage. Source unknown, but of Pueblo design. X-1976.4, .5.

*454. **Necklace,** silver, length 70.0. Hand-hammered beads with 22 "squash blossom" pendants and central "naja" pendant. Navajo tribe, late XIX or early XX c. Gift of Amelia Elizabeth White, 1937.606.

455. **Bracelet,** silver, width .30. Incised chevrons. Navajo tribe, about 1880. Gift of Thomas Cleneay, 1887.20662.

456. **Bracelet,** silver and turquoise, width 3.8. Studded with three turquoises with diamond-shaped design around each. Navajo tribe, late XIX or early XX c. Gift of Amelia Elizabeth White, 1937.601.

457. **Bracelet,** silver and turquoise, width 2.5. Central oval turquoise flanked by two square turquoises with stamped designs surrounding them. Navajo tribe, late XIX or early XX c. Gift of Amelia Elizabeth White, 1937.603.

458. **Bracelet,** silver and turquoise, width 3.1. Central oval turquoise surrounded by stamped designs. Navajo tribe, late XIX or early XX c. Gift of Amelia Elizabeth White, 1937.604.

459. **Bracelet,** silver and turquoise, width 3.0. Openwork design of silver wire centered with an oval turquoise. Navajo tribe, probably 1920's. Gift of Mrs. Frank Seinsheimer, Sr., 1944.97.

460. **Bracelet,** silver and turquoise, width 1.2. Rope design of twisted silver wire with three turquoises set on silver bases. Navajo tribe or Zuni Pueblo, late XIX or early XX c. Gift of Amelia Elizabeth White, 1937.602.

461. **Basket-Bowl,** yucca and willow (?), height 10.9, diameter 39.0. Coiled construction with design of red, blue and green. Jicarilla Apache tribe, New Mexico, XX c. Gift of Amelia Elizabeth White, 1937.510.

462. **Storage Basket-Jar,** willow and devil's claw, height 23.0, diameter 24.2. Coiled construction, pattern of vertical zigzags, crosses and human figures. Apache tribe, Arizona, XIX c. Gift of James W. Bullock, 1907.149.

463. **Storage Basket-Jar,** willow and devil's claw, height 35.8, diameter 25.0. Coiled construction, pattern of animals and human figures. Apache tribe, Arizona, XIX c. Gift of Mrs. William N. King, 1926.38.

464. **Basket-Jar,** willow and devil's claw, height 17.9, diameter 13.4. Coiled construction, pattern of stripes, human and animal figures. Apache tribe, Arizona, XIX c. Gift of Mrs. William N. King, 1924.179.

465. **Basket-Bowl,** willow and devil's claw, height 9.0, diameter 20.9. Coiled construction, pattern of figures, crosses and geometric shapes. Apache tribe, Arizona, XIX c. Gift of Mrs. William N. King, 1924.180.

466. **Carrying Basket,** willow, devil's claw and leather, height 33.2, diameter 40.0. Twined construction with horizontal bands and red and yellow paint on dark bands; lower part covered with painted yellow hide and fringe; cloth handle held by leather loops. Apache tribe, Arizona, XIX c. Gift of Estate of Nettleton Neff, 1940.1215.

467. **Water Jar,** willow (?), height 35.7, diameter 33.2, Diagonal twined weave, covered with pine gum and bone marrow; calico carrier-strap from twig handles. Apache tribe, Arizona, XIX c. Gift of Estate of Nettleton Neff, 1940.1216.

468. **Basket,** yucca, height 11.5, diameter 40.7. Three-rod coiled construction with 5-pointed "star" design in center. Mescalero Apache tribe, New Mexico, XIX c. Gift of William N. King, 1906.99.

469. **Basket,** yucca, height 11.5, diameter 48.4. Coiled construction, human figures and animal forms. Mescalero Apache tribe, New Mexico, XIX c. Gift of William N. King, 1906.100.

470. **Basket,** willow and devil's claw, height 7.7, diameter 42.1. Three-rod coil construction with

a design of triangles. Chiricahua Apache tribe, Arizona, XIX c. Gift of William N. King, 1906.106.

471. **Basket,** willow and devil's claw, height 10.2, diameter 37.0. Coiled construction, "whirlwind" and man-bird pattern. Chiricahua Apache tribe, Arizona, XIX c. Gift of William N. King. 1906.107.

*472. **Grain Storage Basket-Jar,** willow and devil's claw, height 40.8, diameter 37.0. Coiled construction, with pattern of humans, animals and rectangles. San Carlos Apache tribe, Arizona, XIX c. Gift of William N. King, 1906.102.

473. **Basket-Tray,** willow and devil's claw, height 5.7, diameter 38.4. Coiled construction, "whirling wheel" pattern. San Carlos Apache tribe, Arizona, XIX c. Gift of William N. King, 1906.105.

*474. **Basket-Plaque,** yucca, diameter 59.8. Coiled, the kachina "Crow Mother" design woven in multicolor dyed fibers. From Hopi area, Second Mesa, Arizona, XIX c. Gift of Mrs. Georgine Holmes Thomas, 1910.548.

475. **Basket-Tray,** yucca, height 3.2, diameter 28.7. Coiled with design of kachina (?) woven in multicolor dyed fibers. From Hopi area, Second Mesa, Arizona, XIX c., collected by Major J. W. Powell, 1874. Gift of United States National Museum, 1889.69.

476. **Basket-Tray,** yucca, height 6.3, diameter 39.7. Coiled design of 8-pointed "star" in multicolor dyed fibers. From Hopi area, Second Mesa, XIX c., collected by J. E. Stevenson, 1885-1886. Gift of United States National Museum, 1889.68.

477. **Basket-Tray,** sumac twigs, height 7.6, diameter 40.9. Wicker-plaited with whipped rim of yucca. From Hopi area; Third Mesa, XIX c., collected by V. Mindeleff, 1883. Gift of United States National Museum, 1889.65.

478. **Utility Basket-Bowl,** sumac twigs, height 8.8, diameter 40.7. Wicker-weave with whipped rim of yucca. From Hopi area, Third Mesa, Late XIX or early XX c. Gift of James W. Bullock, 1907.157.

479. **Basket-Tray,** sumac twigs, height 2.5, diameter 30.6. Wicker-weave with band design of dyed multicolors. From Hopi area, Third Mesa, XIX c., collected by Mrs. J. E. Stevenson, 1885-1886. Gift of United States National Museum, 1889.67.

480. **Basket-Tray,** sumac twigs, height 4.4, diameter 31.9. Wicker-weave with band design of dyed multicolors. From Hopi area, Third Mesa, XIX c., collected by Mrs. J. E. Stevenson, 1885-1886. Gift of United States National Museum, 1889.66.

481. **Basket-Water Jar,** height 23.0, diameter 23.0. Coiled, applied pitch; two horsehair handles with leather strap. From Hopi area, Oraibi, Third Mesa, Arizona, XIX c. Gift of United States National Museum, 1889.73.

482. **Basket with Lid,** rectangular, yucca, height 17.9 by 17.0 by 19.0. Heavy coiled construction with multicolored patches; coiled lid. From Hopi area, XIX c. Gift of Mrs. Georgine Holmes Thomas, 1910.549.

483. **Basket-Bowl,** sumac and mountain mahogany, height 8.2, diameter 34.0. Coiled, pattern of triangles and a brown band. Navajo tribe, Arizona, XIX c. Gift of Eleanor I. Earnshaw, 1912.355.

484. **Basket-Bowl,** sumac and mountain mahogany, height 10.0, diameter 38.5. Coiled with a 9 "petal" pattern of brown. Navajo or Jicarilla Apache tribe, XIX c. Gift of William N. King, 1906.97.

485. **Basket-Bowl,** sumac and mountain mahogany, height 12.0, diameter 40.7. Coiled with a pattern of triangles and a brown band. Navajo tribe, Arizona, XIX c. Gift of George W. Lewis for Annie K. Laws, 1928.242.

486. **Basket-Bowl,** sumac, height 10.0, diameter 39.7. Coiled with a pattern of dyed navy and red. Made by the Paiute tribe for Navajo usage, XX c. Gift of Amelia Elizabeth White, 1937.509.

487. **"Ring" Carrying Basket,** yucca and sumac, height 17.8, diameter 48.5. Twilled plaiting is bent over a hoop and fastened with twining. From Pueblo area, XIX c., collected by J. E. Stevenson, 1885. Gift of United States National Museum, 1889.75.

488. **Basket-Bowl,** bear grass core, willow and devil's claw, height 7.6, diameter 30.7. Coiled with a six-pointed "Star" and "petal" design. Papago tribe, Arizona, XIX c. Gift of James W. Bullock, 1907.165.

489. **Basket,** cattail core, split willow, devil's claw, height 7.6, diameter 21.7. Coiled with "turtle" pattern. Pima tribe, Arizona, XIX c. Gift of William N. King, 1906.110.

490. **Basket,** cattail core, split willow, devil's claw, height 10.1, diameter 24.2. Coiled with design of alternating human figures and realistic horses. Pima tribe, Arizona, late XIX c. Gift of William N. King, 1906.109.

491. **Basket-Bowl,** cattail core, split willow, devil's claw, height 10.1, diameter 34.5. Coiled with "labyrinth" design. Pima tribe, Arizona, XIX c. Gift of James W. Bullock, 1907.164.

492. **Basket,** cattail core, split willow, devil's claw, height 8.9, diameter 11.3. Coiled with design of six human figures. Pima tribe, Arizona, late XIX or early XX c. Gift of William N. King, 1906.111.

493. **Basket-Jar,** cattail core and willow, height 21.7, diameter 21.7. Coiled with red color applied in vertical stripes. Pima tribe, Arizona, XIX c. Gift of William N. King, 1906.108.

*494. **Basket-Bowl,** willow with devil's claw, height 11.5, diameter 38.5. Coiled, crenelated geometric pattern. Maricopa tribe, Arizona, XIX c. Gift of James W. Bullock, 1907.162.

495. **Utility Basket,** oval, willow, height 29.3 by 21.5 by 16.7. Wicker-plaited with uncut-edge uprights (bams) at top, used for gathering clay for pottery. Zuni Pueblo, New Mexico, XIX c. Gift of James W. Bullock, 1907.129.

496. **Basket-Bowl,** willow and yucca, height 6.0, diameter 29.0. Coiled, faint pattern of two human (?) figures. Zuni Pueblo, New Mexico, XIX c., collected by Major J. W. Powell. Gift of United States National Museum, 1889.71.

*497. **Drumstick,** wood with leather binding, length 39.5. Stick is curved to form a loop at one end, lashed down with thong. Zuni Pueblo, New Mexico, XIX c. Gift of General M. F. Force, 1894.252.

498. **Chanting Drum,** painted rawhide on wooden frame, depth 7.0, diameter 23.0. One side covered with rawhide with red, yellow and blue pattern. Apache tribe, XIX c. Gift of William H. Doane, 1914.110.

499. **Dance Shield,** painted rawhide with hawk and eagle feathers, diameter 38.5. Red circle in center, green and red border, feather edging, leather thongs. From Pueblo area (?), XIX c. Gift of J. H. Sharp, 1905.366.

*500. **Parfleche,** painted rawhide, 35.8 by 77.7. Unusual proportions when folded, zigzags and dots of black, red and green. Jicarilla Apache tribe (?), XX c. Gift of Amelia Elizabeth White, 1937.557.

501. **Weft Knife,** wood, 28.0 by 5.0. Used to force weft strands in position on a belt loom. Zuni Pueblo, New Mexico, XIX c., collected by James E. Stevenson, 1884. Gift of United States National Museum, 1889.106.

502. **Loom Roller,** wood, length 21.5, diameter 5.5. Used to spread warps on a belt loom, cords attached around knobs at each end fasten in

back of weaver and finished weaving is wound on roller. Zuni Pueblo, New Mexico, XIX c., collected by James E. Stevenson, 1884. Gift of United States National Museum, 1889.107.

503. **Pump Drill,** wood with iron tip and stone disk weight, length 43.5. Used to drill holes in turquoise and other objects for jewelry. From Hopi area, Arizona, XIX c. Gift of General M. F. Force, 1894.158.

504. **Ladle,** sheep horn, length 26.0. From Hopi area, Arizona, XIX c., collected by Major J. W. Powell. Gift of United States National Museum, 1889.102.

505. **Ceremonial Dance Bow,** painted wood, length 83.0. Simple curve with remnants of brilliant red, green and black paint on inner side. Zuni Pueblo, New Mexico, XIX c., collected by James E. Stevenson, 1884. Gift of United States National Museum, 1889.112.

506. **Feather Box and Lid,** rectangular, 7.0 by 44.5 by 7.5. Solid piece of wood with small extension and thong handle at one end; separate lid held on with thongs. Used for sacred plumes and prayer sticks of the sacred societies. Zuni Pueblo, New Mexico, XIX c. Gift of General M. F. Force, 1894.172.

507. **Rabbit Stick,** painted wood, length 63.0. Flat, double-curved, center area stained orange with black painted stripes; used to bring down small game. From Hopi area, Arizona, collected by Dr. E. Palmer, 1870. Gift of United States National Museum, 1889.115.

508. **Kachina,** painted cottonwood, height 26.0. Probably Angokchina (the long-haired kachina); dressed in kilt, sash and necklace with naja, holding a basket in left hand. From Hopi tribe, Arizona, late XIX c. Gift of Mrs. Charles Fleischmann, 1911.1684.

The Ancient Midwest

Paleo-Indian

509. **Fluted Projectile Point,** flint, length 6.9. From Ohio. Gift of Thomas Cleneay, 1887.12237.

*510. **Fluted Projectile Point,** flint, length 6.9. From Kenton County, Kentucky. Gift of Thomas Cleneay, 1887.4974.

*511. **Fluted Projectile Point,** flint, length 7.0. From Kenton County, Kentucky. Gift of Thomas Cleneay, 1887.4632.

512. **Fluted Projectile Point,** flint, length 10.0. From Boone County, Kentucky. Gift of Thomas Cleneay, 1887.5790.

513. **Fluted Projectile Point,** flint probably from Flint Ridge, Ohio, length 10.1. From Boone County, Kentucky. Gift of Thomas Cleneay, 1887.5174.

514. **Fluted Projectile Point,** flint, length 8.5. From Aurora, Indiana. Gift of Thomas Cleneay, 1887.14122.

515. **Fluted Projectile Point,** flint, length 10.8. From the Ohio River bank between Aurora, Indiana, and Louisville, Kentucky. Gift of Thomas Cleneay, 1887.13570.

*516. **Fluted Projectile Point,** flint, length 10.5. From the Ohio River bank above Maysville, Kentucky. Gift of Thomas Cleneay, 1887.12975.

517. **Fluted Projectile Point,** flint, length 8.5. From West Virginia. Gift of Thomas Cleneay, 1887.14783.

518. **Fluted Projectile Point,** flint, length 7.1. From Green Bottom, West Virginia. Gift of Thomas Cleneay, 1887.14757.

*519. **Fluted Cumberland Fishtail Point,** flint, length 13.9. From Missouri. Gift of Thomas Cleneay, 1887.14787.

520. **Fluted Projectile Point,** flint, length 10.5. From Missouri. Gift of Thomas Cleneay, 1887.14789.

Early Archaic

521. **Dovetail Point,** flint, length 9.0. From Columbia, Ohio (now East End of Cincinnati). Gift of Thomas Cleneay, 1887.3324.

522-523. **Dovetail Points,** flint, length 11.4, 9.5. From Aurora, Indiana. Gift of Thomas Cleneay, 1887.13751, .13764.

524. **Dovetail Point,** flint, length 8.6. From Big Bone Lick, Kentucky. Gift of Thomas Cleneay, 1887.12358.

525-526. **Dovetail Points,** flint, length 11.3, 13.5. Source unknown, 1938.5204, .3363.

527. **Dovetail Point,** flint probably from Flint Ridge, Ohio, length 13.1. Source unknown, 1938.5162.

528. **Dovetail Point,** flint, length 8.5. From Bourbon County, Kentucky. Gift of Thomas Cleneay, 1887.14554.

*529. **Lance Point,** flint, length 8.7. From Brown County, Ohio. Gift of Thomas Cleneay, 1887.15098.

*530. **Beaver Lake Point,** flint, length 8.2 From Boone County, Kentucky. Gift of Thomas Cleneay, 1887.5903.

*531. **Projectile Point,** flint, length 6.8. From the Kentucky River valley below Frankfort. Gift of Thomas Cleneay, 1887.19564.

532. **Plainview Point,** flint, length, 5.7. From Boone County, Kentucky. Gift of Thomas Cleneay, 1887.5436.

533. **Projectile Point,** flint, length 6.0. From Boone County, Kentucky. Gift of Thomas Cleneay, 1887.5465.

534. **Projectile Point,** flint, length 12.0. From "The Wild Kentuckian." Gift of Thomas Cleneay. 1887.19198.

535. **Projectile Point,** flint, length 9.5. From Powhatan, Belmont County, Ohio. Gift of Thomas Cleneay, 1887.18339.

536-538. **Projectile Points,** flint, length 10.5, 10.2, 7.5. From Alton, Illinois. Gift of Thomas Cleneay, 1887.6606, .6578, .6586.

*539. **Dalton Point,** flint, length 5.7. From Alton, Illinois. Gift of Thomas Cleneay, 1887.6518.

*540. **Dalton Point,** flint, length 5.7. Source unknown. 1938.5251.

541. **Yuma Point,** flint, length 9.3. From Alton, Illinois. Gift of Thomas Cleneay, 1887.6593.

542. **Angostura Point,** flint, length 8.1. Source unknown. Gift of Thomas Cleneay, 1887.16299.

*543. **Kirk Point,** flint, length 6.1. From Columbia, Ohio (now East End of Cincinnati). Gift of Thomas Cleneay, 1887.3764.

544-545. **Kirk Points,** flint, length 3.7, 7.8. From Kenton County, Kentucky. Gift of Thomas Cleneay, 1887.4899, .4728.

546. **Kirk Point,** length 5.1. From Milton, Kentucky. Gift of Thomas Cleneay, 1887.19400.

547-550. **Kirk Points,** flint, length 6.7, 6.0, 5.9, 5.7. From Taylor's Creek, Kentucky. Gift of Thomas Cleneay, 1887.229, .617, .159, .154.

*551-552. **Agate Basin Points,** flint, length 10.5, 9.2. Source unknown, 1938.3184, .4849.

*553. **Thebes Knife or Javelin Blade,** flint, length 10.7. From Hamilton County, Ohio. Gift of Thomas Cleneay, 1887.6079.

554. **Knife or Javelin Blade** related to Thebes type, length 5.9. From the Ohio River bank opposite New Richmond, Ohio, collected 1871 by Samuel Peden of New Richmond. Gift of Thomas Cleneay, 1887.6319.

555. **Projectile Point,** flint, length 8.9, Early to Middle Archaic. Source unknown. Gift of Thomas Cleneay, 1887.19026.

Middle Archaic

556. **Kanawha Stemmed Point,** flint, length 3.9. From the Ohio River bank. Gift of Thomas Cleneay, 1887.8939.

*557. **Kanawha Stemmed Point,** flint, length 3.7. From Milford, Ohio. Gift of Thomas Cleneay, 1887.19728.

558. **Le Croy Point, flint,** length 2.7. From the Ohio River bank opposite New Richmond, Ohio. Gift of Thomas Cleneay, 1887.6285.

*559. **Le Croy Point,** flint, length 3.4. Source unknown. Gift of Thomas Cleneay, 1887.16392.

560. **Le Croy Point,** flint, length 4.1. Source unknown. 1938. 3615.

*561. **Eva Knife or Spear Blade,** flint, length, 11.0. From Alton, Illinois. Gift of Thomas Cleneay, 1887.6391.

562. **Big Sandy Knife or Spear Blade,** flint, length 9.9. From Alton, Illinois. Gift of Thomas Cleneay, 1887.6360.

*563. **Cypress Creek I Knife or Spear Blade,** flint, length 9.5. Source unknown, 1938.3310.

564. **Cypress Creek I Knife or Spear Blade,** flint, length 11.3. From Lower Blue Licks, Kentucky 1884. Gift of Thomas Cleneay, 1887.18314.

565. **Cypress Creek I Knife or Spear Blade,** flint, length 7.5. From Boone County, Kentucky. Gift of Thomas Cleneay, 1887.5675.

566. **Lost Lake Knife or Spear Blade,** flint, length 8.7. From Columbia, Ohio (now East End of Cincinnati). Gift of Thomas Cleneay, 1887.3310.

*567. **Full-Grooved Axe,** basic igneous rock, 17.9 by 12.4 by 7.2. From Massachusetts. Gift of Thomas Cleneay, 1887.15270.

*568. **Unfinished Bannerstone Showing Start of Drilling,** granite, length 6.5. From California, Kentucky. Gift of Thomas Cleneay, 1887.9634.

569. **Unfinished Bannerstone,** quartzite, length 6.5. Source unknown, but once in the collection of Dorfeuille's Museum, Cincinnati. Gift of Thomas Cleneay, 1887.12458.

Late Archaic

*570. **Tubular Pipe,** muddy limestone, length 9.5. Source unknown. Gift of Thomas Cleneay, 1887.18949.

*571. **Bell Pestle,** quartzite, length 15.5. Source unknown. Gift of Thomas Cleneay, 1887.15101.

572. **Bell Pestle,** quartzite, length 14.0. Source unknown. Gift of Dr. S. C. Heighway, 1937.7094.

*573. **Roller Pestle,** coarse sandstone, length 29.4. From Decatur County, Indiana. Gift of Thomas Cleneay, 1887.12764.

574. **Nutstone,** coarse sandstone, length 25.5. Source unknown. Gift of Thomas Cleneay, 1887.16275.

575. **Pendant,** slate, length 10.8. From Big Bone Lick, Kentucky. Gift of Thomas Cleneay, 1887.20042.

576. **Pendant,** slate, length 12.6. Source unknown. Gift of Thomas Cleneay, 1887.20822.

577. **Gorget,** slate, length 13.1. Source unknown, 1938.5170.

578. **Pendant,** slate, length 5.0. From Mason County, West Virginia. Gift of Thomas Cleneay, 1887.15197.

579. **Pendant with Serrated Lower Edge and Incised Zoned Hatching on one side,** slate, length 4.2. From the Ohio River bank above Maysville, Kentucky. Gift of Thomas Cleneay, 1887.13050.

580. **Pendant with Serrated Top Edge and Two Horizontal Grooves,** slate, length 6.4. Source unknown. 1938.2734.

581. **Pendant with Incised Zigzag and Notched Edges,** slate, length 11.1. Source unknown. 1938.5325.

582. **Pendant,** slate, length 10.6. From Seneca County, Ohio. Gift of Thomas Cleneay, 1887.16250.

583. **Pendant with Serrated Lower Edge,** slate, length 9.7. Found on Indian Creek, Hamilton County, Ohio. Gift of Thomas Cleneay, 1887.6020.

584. **Pendant,** slate, length 8.0. From Hamilton County, Ohio. Gift of Thomas Cleneay, 1887.6018.

585. **Pendant,** slate, length 12.2. From Ashland County, Ohio. Gift of Thomas Cleneay, 1887.16242.

586. **Pendant,** granite, length 9.8. From West Virginia. Gift of Thomas Cleneay, 1887.14712.

*587. **Gorget,** slate, length 13.9. From Big Bone Lick, Kentucky. Gift of Thomas Cleneay, 1887.20043.

588. **Unfinished Stemmed Point Before Forming of Stem,** flint, length 14.0. Source unknown, 1938.5195.

*589. **Hemphill Point,** flint, length 12.0. From Alton, Illinois. Gift of Thomas Cleneay, 1887.6398.

590. **Projectile Point,** flint, length 6.0. Source unknown. 1938.5141.

591. **Projectile Point or Blade,** flint, length 14.4. From the mouth of the Kentucky River. Gift of Thomas Cleneay, 1887.19348.

592. **Ace of Spades Point,** flint, length 7.2. Source unknown. Gift of Thomas Cleneay, 1887.16286.

593. **Projectile Point,** flint, length 4.9. From the Great Miami River. Gift of Thomas Cleneay, 1887.6857.

*594. **Godar Point,** flint, length 6.8. From Moscow, Ohio. Gift of Thomas Cleneay, 1887.20895.

595. **Projectile Point,** flint, length 4.6. From Aurora, Indiana. Gift of Thomas Cleneay, 1887.14093.

596. **Projectile Point or Knife Blade,** flint, length 11.9. From Alton, Illinois. Gift of Thomas Cleneay, 1887.6625.

597. **Projectile Point or Knife Blade,** flint, length 6.6. From Kenton County, Kentucky. Gift of Thomas Cleneay, 1887.5038.

598. **Projectile Point or Knife Blade,** flint, length 8.2. From the mouth of the Kentucky River. Gift of Thomas Cleneay, 1887.19342.

599. **Projectile Point or Knife Blade,** flint, length 11.4. From Aurora, Indiana, 1880. Gift of Thomas Cleneay, 1887.13780.

600. **Lamoka Point,** flint, length 5.5. From Taylor's Creek, Kentucky. Gift of Thomas Cleneay, 1887.207.

601. **Hardin Backed Point,** flint, length 10.7. From Alton, Illinois. Gift of Thomas Cleneay,1887.6596.

602. **Projectile Point Reworked as a Scraper,** flint, length 4.5. Source unknown. Gift of Dr. S. C. Heighway, 1937.6391.

603. **Projectile Point Reworked as a Scraper,** flint, length 4.0. Source unknown. Gift of Dr. S. C. Heighway, 1937.6396.

604. **Projectile Point,** flint, length 5.8 From Alton, Illinois. Gift of Thomas Cleneay, 1887.6357.

605. **Projectile Point,** flint, length 17.0. Source unknown. 1938.5180.

606. **Projectile Point,** jasper, length 4.1. From Boone County, Kentucky. Gift of Thomas Cleneay, 1887.5554.

607. **Three-Quarter Grooved Axe,** basic igneous rock, 26.8 by 17.2 by 9.7. Source unknown. Gift of Dr. S. C. Heighway, 1937.7072.

608. **Three-Quarter Grooved Ave,** basic igneous rock, 7.6. by 5.3 by 3.2. Source unknown. Gift of Dr. S. C. Heighway, 1937.7062.

*609. **Three-Quarter Grooved Axe,** basic igneous rock, probably gabbro, 16.9 by 9.3 by 7.4. From California, Kentucky. Gift of Thomas Cleneay, 1887.9645.

610. **Adze,** igneous rock, length 21.5. From the bank of the Ohio River between Cincinnati, Ohio, and Maysville, Kentucky. Gift of Thomas Cleneay, 1887.12687.

611. **Adze,** granite, length 10.0. Source unknown. 1938.4542.

612. **Adze,** basic igneous rock, length 6.6. Source unknown. Gift of Harry Zerring, 1918.71.

613. **Adze,** basic igneous rock, length 4.9. From Pickaway County, Ohio. Gift of Thomas Cleneay, 1887.16236.

614. **Adze,** hematite, length 6.0. Source unknown. Gift of Dr. S. C. Heighway, 1937.3639.

615. **Adze,** hematite, length 3.3. Source unknown. Gift of Thomas Cleneay, 1887.19971.

*616. **Birdstone,** slate, length 14.9. Source unknown, but probably a surface find in the vicinity of Cincinnati. Gift of Judge Joseph Cox, 1888.512.

617. **Birdstone,** slate, length 7.2. From Lower Blue Licks, Kentucky. Gift of Thomas Cleneay, 1887.18313.

618. **Birdstone,** granite, length 8.2. Source unknown. 1938.5133.

*619. **Lozenge-Shaped Bannerstone,** banded slate, length 17.2. From Campbell County, Kentucky. Gift of Thomas Cleneay, 1887.9453.

*620. **Crescent-Shaped Bannerstone,** banded slate, length 13.0. From Big Bone Lick, Kentucky. Gift of Thomas Cleneay, 1887.20020.

621. **Crescent-Shaped Bannerstone,** banded slate, length 10.0. Source unknown, but collected by Museum members in Ohio River valley, 1918.5646.

622. **Tubular Bannerstone with Expanded Ends,** banded slate, length 7.2. From Fort Ancient, Ohio. Gift of Thomas Cleneay, 1887.12634.

623. **Tubular Bannerstone,** banded slate, length 9.7. From Marion, Ohio. Gift of Thomas Cleneay, 1887.16214.

624. **Bannerstone,** banded slate, length 8.2 From the Ohio River valley opposite Aurora, Indiana. Gift of Thomas Cleneay, 1887.8696.

625. **Shuttle-Shaped Bannerstone,** banded slate, length 14.7. From Bourbon County, Kentucky. Gift of Thomas Cleneay, 1887.14595.

626. **H-Shaped Bannerstone,** banded slate, length 13.8. From New Richmond, Ohio, 1873. Gift of Thomas Cleneay, 1887.6216.

627. **Spherical Bannerstone,** banded slate, diameter 5.7. Source unknown. Gift of Thomas Cleneay, 1887.19254.

628. **Claw-Shaped Bannerstone,** banded slate, length 10.2. Found near Harrison, Indiana. Gift of Thomas Cleneay, 1887.14133.

629. **Plummet,** stone not identifiable from present surface appearance, length 8.0. From Big Bone Lick, Kentucky. Gift of Thomas Cleneay, 1887.20060.

630. **Plummet,** hematite, length 5.0. Source unknown. Gift of Thomas Cleneay, 1887.20645.

631. **Plummet,** hematite, length 4.0. Source unknown. Gift of Thomas Cleneay, 1887.18972.

632. **Plummet,** hematite or a ferruginous concretion, length 4.8. Source unknown. Gift of Thomas Cleneay, 1887.19175.

633. **Plummet,** granite, length 8.4. Source unknown. 1938.5328.

634. **Plummet,** cherty hematite, length 7.5. Source unknown. Gift of Thomas Cleneay, 1887.19928.

635. **Spherical Ball,** sandstone, diameter 7.6. From Boone County, Kentucky, 1875. Gift of Thomas Cleneay, 1887.5969.

636. **Spherical Ball,** probably limestone rounded naturally by stream action, diameter 5.0. Source unknown. 1938.3821.

637. **Spherical Ball,** igneous rock, diameter 5.0. Source unknown. 1938.3827.

638. **Spherical Ball,** sandstone, diameter 7.0. Source unknown. 1938.8306.

639. **Disk Pendant,** shell not readily identifiable in present state, but probably from a marine mollusk, diameter 5.7-6.5. Source unknown, but probably originated in the Glacial Kame area along the Ohio-Michigan line. Bequest of Harry Zerring, 1918.287.

*640. **Long Tubular Beads,** cut from the columella of the marine mollusk Busycon, length 10-11. From C. West, Cleves, Ohio. Gift of Thomas Cleneay, 1887.9593.

*641. **Disk Beads,** shell, diameter about .60. From Big Bone Lick, Kentucky. Gift of Thomas Cleneay, 1887.20083.

*642. **Pendant,** Busycon columella, length 8.3. From the Kentucky River below Frankfort. Gift of Thomas Cleneay, 1887.19550.

643. **Thin Tubular Beads,** shell, average length about 2.5. Source unknown, once in collection of R. K. Crane. Gift of Thomas Cleneay, 1887.17219.

644. **Scraper,** flint, length 7.0. Source unknown. Gift of Dr. S. C. Heighway, 1937.3405.

645. **Projectile Point Reworked to Make a Projectile Shaft Scraper,** flint, length 4.6. From Boone County, Kentucky, 1872. Gift of Thomas Cleneay, 1887.5178.

646. **Projectile Point Reworked to Form an End Scraper,** flint, length 3.2. Source unknown. Gift of Dr. S. C. Heighway, 1937.6428.

647. **Projectile Point Reworked to Form a Concave Scraper,** flint, length 4.5. Source unknown. Gift of Thomas Cleneay, 1887.16928.

648. **Long Curving Blade Scraper,** flint, length 16.2. From Ohio County, Indiana. Gift of Thomas Cleneay, 1887.13600.

649. **Scraper,** flint, probably from Flint Ridge, Ohio, length 4.7. Source unknown. Gift of Thomas Cleneay, 1887.17004.

650. **Side Scraper,** flint, length 5.5. From Indiana. Gift of Thomas Cleneay, 1887.11558.

651. **Side Scraper,** flint probably from Flint Ridge, Ohio, length 9.6 From Ohio County, Indiana. Gift of Thomas Cleneay, 1887.13601.

652. **End Scraper,** flint, length 6.6. From Indiana. Gift of Thomas Cleneay, 1887.11541.

653. **Scraper,** flint, length 7.8. From Madison, Indiana. Gift of Thomas Cleneay, 1887.11458.

Early Woodland — Adena

*654. **Celt,** ground and polished igneous rock, length 11.6. Source unknown. Gift of Thomas Cleneay, 1887.1772.

655. **Boatstone,** bedded standstone, length 8.0, perforated. Source unknown. 1938.3171.

*656. **Boatstone Fragment,** marbleized limestone with incrustations, length 6.6. From the Ohio River valley above Portsmouth, Ohio, once in the Crockett collection, Portsmouth. Gift of Thomas Cleneay, 1887.19600.

*657. **Tubular Pipe,** probably Ohio pipestone, length 20.3. From Kentucky. Gift of Dr. S. C. Heighway, 1937.6622.

658. **Knife Blade,** flint, length 13.5. From Oxbows, Indiana. Gift of Thomas Cleneay, 1887.3991.

659. **Knife Blade,** flint, length 19.1. From Columbia, Ohio (now East End of Cincinnati). Gift of Thomas Cleneay, 1887.3315.

660. **Native Copper Adze Blade,** length 14.1. From the banks of the Kentucky River below Frankfort. Gift of Thomas Cleneay, 1887.20649.

661. **Native Copper Adze Blade,** length 4.6. From Henry County, Indiana. Gift of Thomas Cleneay, 1887.20650.

*662. **Native Copper Adze Blade,** length 10.1. From Henry County, Indiana. Gift of Thomas Cleneay, 1887.20648.

*663-665. **Lumps of Red Ochre,** average length 4.5. Source unknown. Gift of Thomas Cleneay, 1887.12665, .19932, .19941.

*666. **The Waverly Tablet,** shale ground and engraved with symbols of a raptorial bird (?), 8.6 by 6.6 by 0.8. Found in 1885 by Abraham Cutlip when leveling a mound on his farm between Waverly and Piketon, Ohio; purchased (?) from Cutlip by Dr. W. R. Hurst, Piketon; purchased from Dr. Hurst by J. R. MacLean; purchased from MacLean by Robert Clarke of Cincinnati; lent by Clarke to the Cincinnati Art Museum, 1890; given to the Museum by his niece Mrs. William N. Galt, 1939.140. Published: J. Ralston Skinner, "The Identification of the British Inch...", *Journal of the Cincinnati Society of Natural History,* IX, 4, 1886-7, p. 240, fig. 14; W. H. Holmes, "Certain Notched or Scalloped Stone Tablets of the Mound Builders," *American Anthropologist,* 1906, p. 102; W. H. Holmes, "Notched Plates," *Bulletin 30, Part 2: Handbook of American Indians North of Mexico,* Bureau of American Ethnology, Washington, 1910, p. 86; Gordon R. Willey and Jeremy A. Sabloff, *A History of American Archaeology,* San Francisco, W. H. Reem, 1974, fig. 38, p. 56.

667. **Bust-Type Birdstone,** fine-grained sandstone, length 4.8. Late Adena or early Hopewell. Source unknown. Gift of Dr. S. C. Heighway, 1937.2900.

668. **Blocked-End Pipe,** clay, length 11.8. From the vicinity of Cincinnati. Gift of Judge Joseph Cox, 1888.336.

669-672. **Hematite Cones,** height 2.5-3.0. From Bourbon County, Kentucky, 1887.14597, .14600. From the Ohio River bank between Portsmouth and the Big Kanawha, 1887.18381. From Chillicothe, Ohio, 1887.12484. Gift of Thomas Cleneay.

673. **Celt, hematite,** length 5.6. Source unknown. Gift of Thomas Cleneay, 1887.19008.

674. **Celt,** hematite, length 2.0. Source unknown. Gift of Thomas Cleneay, 1887.20654.

*675. **Native Copper Rectangular Gorget,** 10.8 by 6.6. From Racine, Meigs County, Ohio. Gift of General M. F. Force, 1894.491.

*676. **Native Copper Crescent Gorget,** length 14.0. From Ohio. Gift of Mrs. E. L. Flagg, 1882.959.

677. **Native Copper Bracelet,** diameter 6.2-8.0. Source unknown. Gift of Thomas Cleneay, 1887.20663.

*678. **Native Copper Bracelet,** diameter 5.3-6.4. From Henry County, Indiana. Gift of Thomas Cleneay, 1887.20665.

679. **Gorget,** slate, 9.0 by 6.8. From the Ohio River bank between Portsmouth, Ohio, and the Big Kanawha River. Gift of Thomas Cleneay, 1887.18359.

*680. **Gorget,** slate, 11.2 by 8.4. Found at Columbia, Ohio (now East End of Cincinnati), 1874. Gift of Thomas Cleneay, 1887.3796.

*681. **Expanded-Center, Plano-Convex Bar Gorget,** slate, 12.4 by 3.8. Source unknown. 1938-5320.

682. **Pendant,** slate, length 11.6. From Athens County, Ohio. Gift of Thomas Cleneay, 1887.15388.

*683. **Pendant,** slate, length 11.7. Source unknown. Gift of Thomas Cleneay, 1887.20641.

684. **Pendant,** slate, length 9.9. Source unknown. 1938.5318.

685. **Pendant with Notched Top and Bottom Edges,** slate, length 11.5. From Alton, Illinois. Gift of Thomas Cleneay, 1887.6712.

686. **Gorget,** slate, length 10.5. Source unknown. 1938.5168.

687. **Gorget,** banded slate, length 7.9. Source unknown. Gift of Thomas Cleneay, 1887.15134.

688. **Pendant,** igneous rock, length 9.0. From Bourbon County, Kentucky. Gift of Thomas Cleneay, 1887.14592.

689. **Pendant,** slate, length 12.7. Adena or Hopewell. From Big Bone Lick, Kentucky. Gift of Thomas Cleneay, 1887.20022.

690. **Unfinished Reel-Shaped Gorget,** slate, length 7.5. A Late Adena form. Source unknown. 1938.5169.

691. **Pendant,** slate with incrustation in one corner, length 10.9. Source unknown. 1938.5308.

692. **Pendant,** banded slate, length 6.4. From Columbus, Ohio. Gift of Thomas Cleneay, 1887.9606.

*693-696. **Cache of Blades from The Same Flint Nodule,** length 12.5-12.7. From Mr. Terrell, Valley Junction (near present-day Elizabethtown, Ohio). Gift of Thomas Cleneay, 1887.18307, .18308, .18310, .18311.

697-699. **Cache of Blades from The Same Flint Nodule,** length 10.5-13.0. From Jackson County, Indiana. Gift of Thomas Cleneay, 1887.18309, .12429-12433.

700-744. **Cache of Blades,** flint, length 5.8-9.5. From Big Run, Athens County, Ohio. Gift of Thomas Cleneay, 1887.15403-15447.

*745. **Turkey Tail Point,** flint, length 13.8. From Bloomington, Indiana. Gift of Thomas Cleneay, 1887.14962.

746. **Turkey Tail Point,** flint, length 10.4. Source unknown. Gift of Thomas Cleneay, 1887.16290.

747-748. **Turkey Tail Points,** flint, length 12.1, 11.2. Source unknown. 1938.5103, .3377.

749. **Turkey Tail Point,** flint, length 12.5. From Boone County, Kentucky. Gift of Thomas Cleneay, 1887.5915.

750. **Beaver Tail Point,** flint, length 12.6. From Aurora, Indiana. Gift of Thomas Cleneay, 1887.13789.

751. **Beaver Tail Point,** flint probably from Flint Ridge, Ohio, length 11.0. Source unknown, but probably from near Portsmouth, Ohio, once in Crockett collection, Portsmouth. Gift of Thomas Cleneay, 1887.18720.

*752. **Beaver Tail Point,** flint, length 9.7. From Boat Run, Ohio. Gift of Thomas Cleneay, 1887.6202.

753. **Straight-Stemmed Point,** flint, length 8.2. Late Adena to Hopewell. From Bourbon County, Kentucky. Gift of Thomas Cleneay, 1887.14409.

754. **Straight-Stemmed Point,** flint, length 7.3. Source unknown. 1938.3585.

*755. **Robbins Point,** flint, length 10.6. From West Virginia. Gift of Thomas Cleneay, 1887.15540.

756. **Knife Blade,** flint, length 23.5. From Dayton, Kentucky. Gift of Thomas Cleneay, 1887.20909.

757. **Knife Blade,** flint, length 14.0 Source unknown. 1938.5236.

758. **Knife Blade,** flint, length 20.7. From Storrs Township, Hamilton County, Ohio (now Sedamsville area of Cincinnati). Gift of Thomas Cleneay, 1887.4253.

Middle Woodland — Hopewell

*759. **Native Copper Axe Blade,** length 37.8. From Massac County, Illinois. Gift of Thomas Cleneay, 1887.20659.

*760. **Native Copper Stepped Crescent Breastplate with Textile Fragments Adhering Front and Back,** 20.5 by 16.9. Source unknown. 1938.10052.

*761. **Native Copper Rectangular Gorget,** 11.7 by 8.6. From Chillicothe, Ohio. Gift of General M. F. Force, 1894.490.

*762-763. **Native Copper Earspool Disks,** diameter about 4.5-5.0. Source unknown, but collected by Cincinnati Art Museum members in the Ohio River valley. 1918.5808, .5810.

764. **Native Copper Annular Bead,** diameter 1.0. Source unknown, but collected by Museum members in the Ohio River valley, 1918.5837.

765. **Pendant,** green chlorite with mica incrustations, 9.0 by 4.5 by .7. Source unknown. 1938.5312.

766. **Adze Blade,** flint, length 10.5. From Alton, Illinois. Gift of Thomas Cleneay, 1887.6672.

767. **Adze Blade,** flint, length 12.4. From Alton, Illinois. Gift of Thomas Cleneay, 1887.6684.

768. **Gorget,** banded slate, length 8.5. From Lower Blue Lick, Kentucky. Gift of Thomas Cleneay, 1887.18312.

*769. **Gorget,** argillite, length 13.0. Source unknown. 1938.5315.

770. **Pendant,** granite, length 10.5. From Aurora, Indiana. Gift of Thomas Cleneay, 1887.14145.

*771. **Pendant,** banded slate, 12.0 by 6.5. From the Ohio River bank above Maysville, Kentucky. Gift of Thomas Cleneay, 1887.13140.

772. **Hematite Cone,** diameter 4.6. From Kenton County, Kentucky. Gift of Thomas Cleneay, 1887.5154.

773. **Unfinished** Boatstone, granite, length 12.5. From Aurora, Indiana. Gift of Thomas Cleneay, 1887.14158.

774. **Unfinished Boatstone,** mudstone, length 12.5. Source unknown. Gift of Thomas Cleneay, 1887.18933.

*775. **Curved-Platform Pipe,** probably Ohio pipestone, length 9.0. Source unknown. 1938.5013.

*776. **Squared-Poll Celt,** ground igneous rock, length 10.5. From Walnut Hills, Cincinnati, Ohio. Gift of Thomas Cleneay, 1887.20054.

777. **Squared-Poll Celt,** basalt, length 12.7. Source unknown. Gift of Harry Zerring, 1918.104.

778. **Squared-Poll Celt,** basalt, length 16.0. Source unknown, once in the collection of R. H. Warder (?R. B. Warder, Cincinnati Society of Natural History?). Gift of Harry Zerring, 1918.3022.

779. **Bevelled-Poll Celt,** basalt, length 15.9. Source unknown, once in the Warder collection. Gift of Harry Zerring, 1918.3027.

780. **Tapered-Poll Celt,** granite, length 8.9. From the Ohio River bank between Portsmouth, Ohio, and the Big Kanawha. Gift of Thomas Cleneay, 1887.18348.

*781. **Three-Quarter Grooved Axe,** ground and polished granite, length 14.8. From Bourbon County, Kentucky. Gift of Thomas Cleneay, 1887.14590.

*782-793. **Flint Disks From Which Blades and Points would be Struck,** from a cache of 1500 found in 1872 at Beardstown, Illinois, approximate diameters 9.3-15.0. Gift of Thomas Cleneay, 1887.19989-20000.

794. **Knife Blade,** flint, length 8.5. Belmont, Campbell County, Kentucky. Gift of Thomas Cleneay, 1887.12991.

795. **Knife Blade,** flint with crystalline incrustation, length 12.6. Source unknown. 1938.5197.

796. **Knife Blade,** flint, length 9.0. From Big Bone Lick, Kentucky. Gift of Thomas Cleneay, 1887.5916.

*797. **North Cache Point,** flint, length 8.5. From Jackson, Ohio. Gift of Thomas Cleneay, 1887.12459.

*798. **Projectile Point,** flint from Knife River, North Dakota, length 4.7. From Boone County, Kentucky. Gift of Thomas Cleneay, 1887.5716.

799. **Curved Blade,** brown flint probably from Flint Ridge, Ohio, length 12.7. From Mason County, West Virginia. Gift of Thomas Cleneay, 1887.15184.

800. **Knife Blade,** probably Flint Ridge, Ohio, flint, length 9.2. Source unknown. 1938.5202.

801. **Spent Flint Core** from which lamellar blades have been struck, height 6.0. From Kentucky. Gift of Thomas Cleneay, 1887.12154.

802. **Lamellar Blade** struck from a flint nodule like Cat. No. 801, length 5.4. From Fort Ancient, Ohio. Gift of Thomas Cleneay, 1887.12601.

803. **Lamellar Blade** struck from a nodule like Cat. No. 801, of flint from Flint Ridge, Ohio, length 6.9. From Taylor's Creek, Kentucky. Gift of Thomas Cleneay, 1887.515.

804. **Lamellar Blade** struck from a flint nodule like Cat. 801, length 3.5. Source unknown. 1938.7596.

805. **Lamellar Blade** struck from a flint nodule like Cat. No. 801, length 5.5. From Boone County, Kentucky. Gift of Thomas Cleneay, 1887.5782.

806. **Lamellar Blade** struck from a flint nodule like Cat. No. 801, length 6.7. From Pendleton, Ohio (now East End of Cincinnati). Gift of Thomas Cleneay, 1887.2948.

807. **Lamellar Blades** struck from a flint nodule like Cat. No. 801, length 5.3-7.5. From Alton, Illinois. Gift of Thomas Cleneay, 1887.6637, .6640.

808. **Spear or Knife Blade,** flint, length 6.0. From Oxbows, Indiana. Gift of Thomas Cleneay, 1887.3858.

809. **Spear or Knife Blade,** flint, length 10.0. From the Ohio River bank below Louisville, Kentucky. Gift of Thomas Cleneay, 1887.14932.

810. **Spear or Knife Blade,** flint, length 12.2. Source unknown. 1938.3312.

*811. **Ross Barbed Point,** flint, length 12.2. Source unknown. 1938.3322.

812-813. **Spear or Knife Blades,** flint, length 9.5, 6.4. Source unknown. Gift of Dr. S. C. Heighway, 1937.2515, .4276.

*814. **Snyders Point,** flint, length 8.3. From Alton, Illinois. Gift of Thomas Cleneay, 1887.6610.

815. **Spear or Knife Blade,** flint probably from Flint Ridge, Ohio, length 7.0. Source unknown. Gift of Dr. S. C. Heighway, 1937.5922.

816. **Spear or Knife Blade,** Upper Mercer or Zaleski flint, length 10.3. From Athens, Ohio. Gift of Thomas Cleneay, 1887.15430.

*817. **Manker Notched Point,** flint, length 7.1. From Alton, Illinois. Gift of Thomas Cleneay, 1887.6343.

818. **Manker Notched Point,** flint, length 6.4. Source unknown. 1938.6348.

819. **Spear or Knife Blade,** flint, length 11.8. From Indiana. Gift of Thomas Cleneay, 1887.11537.

820. **Spear or Knife Blade,** flint, length 5.7. From Ohio River bank between Aurora, Indiana, and Louisville, Kentucky. Gift of Thomas Cleneay, 1887.13582.

Adena, Hopewell or Mound Intrusive

821. **Knife Blade,** flint, length 6.5. Source unknown. 1938.298.

822. **Knife Blade,** flint, length 7.0. From Kenton County, Kentucky, 1874. Gift of Thomas Cleneay, 1887.5104.

823. **Knife Blade,** flint, length 6.8. Source unknown. Gift of Dr. S. C. Heighway, 1937.6072.

824. **Knife Blade,** flint, length 6.0. Source unknown. Gift of Thomas Cleneay, 1887.16891.

*825. **Platform Pipe,** shale, 6.7 by 4.0. Source unknown, but once in Hall collection. Gift of Thomas Cleneay, 1887.13435.

Late Woodland

*826. **Grasshopper Effigy Pipe,** Lake Superior basalt or gabbro, length 20.2. Source unknown, but relates stylistically to West Central Kentucky or Tennessee in Late Hopewell or Early Late Woodland periods. Gift of Thomas Cleneay, 1887.20683.

*827. **Elbow Pipe,** steatite (probably from an Appalachian quarry), 7.0 by 11.0. From Fayette County, Ohio. Gift of General M. F. Force, 1894.492.

828. **Platform Pipe,** shale, 5.5 by 2.5. Source unknown, 1938.5024.

829. **Platform Pipe,** shale, 5.6 by 2.8. Source unknown, 1938.5167.

830. **Discoidal,** marble, diameter 7.0. Source unknown; once in the collection of Dorfeuille's Museum, Cincinnati. Gift of Thomas Cleneay, 1887.12452.

831. **Discoidal,** granite, diameter 7.2. From Alton, Illinois. Gift of Thomas Cleneay, 1887.6776.

*832. **Tapered-Poll Celt,** banded slate, length 19.3. From the Ohio River valley; once in the Warder collection (Cincinnati ?). Bequest of Harry Zerring, 1918.3030.

*833. **Celt,** flint polished by use to a glassy finish, length 11.6. From Bourbon County, Kentucky. Gift of Thomas Cleneay, 1887.14564.

834. **Celt,** flint from Flint Ridge, Breathit County, Kentucky, length 10.5. From Bourbon County, Kentucky. Gift of Thomas Cleneay, 1887.14568.

835. **Spud,** sandstone, length 25.5. From Clermont County, Ohio. Gift of Thomas Cleneay, 1887.11448.

*836. **Gorget,** banded slate, length 12.9. Source unknown, 1938.5300.

837. **Gorget,** banded slate, length 11.6. Source unknown, 1938.5304.

838. **Projectile Point,** flint, length 5.6. From Hamilton County, Ohio. Gift of Thomas Cleneay, 1887.6057.

839-840. **Projectile Points,** flint, length 5.6, 6.8. From the Ohio River bank. Gift of Thomas Cleneay, 1887.8958, .8950.

841. **Projectile Point,** flint, length 3.0. Source unknown. Gift of Thomas Cleneay, 1887.19053.

*842. **Lowe Flared-Base Point,** flint, length 6.3. Source unknown. Gift of Dr. S. C. Heighway, 1937.4237.

843. **Projectile Point,** flint, length 5.8. Source unknown. Gift of Thomas Cleneay, 1887.16559.

844. **Projectile Point,** flint, length 6.4. Source unknown, once in collection of R. K. Crane. Gift of Thomas Cleneay, 1887.17583.

845. **Projectile Points,** flint, length 6.2, 5.4. Source unknown. 1938.1655, .6196.

846. **Projectile Point,** flint, length 5.4. Source unknown. Gift of Dr. S. C. Heighway, 1937.4316.

847. **Arrowhead,** flint, length 3.0. From Boone County, Kentucky. Gift of Thomas Cleneay, 1887.5188.

848. **Arrowhead,** flint, length 2.4. From Alton, Illinois. Gift of Thomas Cleneay, 1887.6450.

849-850. **Arrowheads,** flint, length 4.2. Source unknown. Gift of Dr. S. C. Heighway, 1937.1869, .4879.

851. **Arrowhead,** quartz, length 3.8. Source unknown. 1938.4810.

*852-854. **Arrowheads,** flint, length 4.6-4.8. Source unknown, 1938.526, .1566, .8277.

Mississippian

*855. **Mask-Gorget,** cut from shell of marine conch, Busycon perversum, height 20.2. Nose and mouth in relief, pierced-hole eyes surrounded by 2 incised circles, upper margin hatched with short incised lines. From Tennessee. Gift of Thomas Cleneay, 1887.20607.

856. **Mask-Gorget with two Quadrupeds Incised on Reverse,** Busycon shell, height 20.0. Pierced-hole eyes, relief mouth and nose, from Tennessee. Gift of Thomas Cleneay, 1887.20615.

857. **Mask-Gorget,** Busycon shell, height 14.4. Pierced-hole eyes surrounded by incised circle, relief nose, hatched top margin. From Tennessee. Gift of Thomas Cleneay, 1887.20613.

858. **Mask-Gorget,** marine shell, probably Busycon but not certainly identifiable from present surface appearance, height 14.0. Pierced-hole eyes. Gift of Thomas Cleneay, 1887.20604.

859. **Mask-Gorget,** marine shell, probably Busycon, height 11.2. Two eye or suspension holes pierced near top margin, top margin hatched with short incised lines. From Tennessee. Gift of Thomas Cleneay, 1887.20601.

860. **Mask-Gorget with Incised Weeping Eye,** marine shell, probably Busycon, height 6.0. Pierced-hole eyes, upper margin hatched with short incised lines and slightly notched, incised line parallel to top margin. From Tennessee. Gift of Thomas Cleneay, 1887.20609.

*861. **Rattlesnake Gorget,** marine shell, probably Busycon, diameter 12.0-14.5. Serpent motif delineated with incised lines and shallow drilled pits, two pierced holes near top margin. From Tennessee. Gift of Thomas Cleneay, 1887.20612.

862. **Gorget,** shell not certainly identifiable from present surface appearance, diameter 8.4-8.8. Perforated and incised decoration combining cross form, cross-hatching, a hand, probably a bird's head and wings. Gift of Thomas Cleneay, 1887.20608.

*863. **Scalloped Gorget,** shell not certainly identifiable from present surface appearance, diameter 7.0-7.8. Incised spiral in center surrounded by circles with drilled-pit centers, two pierced holes near margin. From Tennessee. Gift of Thomas Cleneay, 1887.20616.

*864-865. **Pins** cut from columella of Busycon perversam, length 10.9-14.2. From Tennessee. Gift of Thomas Cleneay, 1887.20619, .20625.

*866. **Mask,** sandstone ground on the obverse, pecked on reverse, height 21.5. Large circular pits for eyes, smaller pit under each eye, nose and lips in relief, grooved around margin. Source unknown, 1938.5124.

867. **Frog Effigy Pipe,** greenish mottled sedimentary bauxitic rock, weathered and partly silicified, probably of lower Mississippi River origin, carved and polished, length 8.3. Source unknown, but vicinity of Cincinnati. Gift of Judge Joseph Cox, 1888.493.

*868. **Chisel,** igneous rock, pecked and ground, length 11.8. From Highland County, Ohio. Gift of Thomas Cleneay, 1887.12736.

869. **Chisel,** black mica schist, ground to a smooth finish, length 23.7. From Columbus, Indiana. Gift of Thomas Cleneay, 1887.20931.

870. **Celt,** flint, chipped, ground and polished from use, length 10.5. From Boone County, Kentucky. Gift of Thomas Cleneay, 1887.5953.

*871. **Hoe Blade,** flint, chipped, ground and polished from use, length 13.5, Cahokia type. Source unknown. Gift of Thomas Cleneay, 1887.20633.

872. **Hoe Blade,** flint probably from the Crescent quarries west of St. Louis, length 18.5. From Alton, Illinois. Gift of Thomas Cleneay, 1887.6762.

873. **Hoe Blade,** flint probably from Crescent quarries, length 14.1. From Alton, Illinois. Gift of Thomas Cleneay, 1887.6755.

874. **Hoe Blade,** chipped flint, polished to glassy sheen from use, length 36.0, Cahokia type. From Alton, Illinois. Gift of Thomas Cleneay, 1887.6812.

875. **Hoe Blade,** flint metamorphosed from fossiliferous Mississippi limestone with micaceous incrustations, chipped and polished to a glassy sheen from use, length 20.2. From Alton, Illinois. Gift of Thomas Cleneay, 1887.6808.

876. **Discoidal,** marble, biconcave pierced, diameter 7.2. From Eagle Creek, Brown County, Ohio. Gift of Thomas Cleneay, 1887.16081.

877. **Discoidal,** marble, diameter 9.0. From Polk County, Tennessee. Gift of Thomas Cleneay, 1887.18278.

878. **Discoidal,** probably quartzite, biconcave pierced, diameter 9.5. From West Virginia. Gift of Thomas Cleneay, 1887.14710.

*879. **Discoidal,** quartzite, biconcave, not pierced, diameter 13.0. From Hamilton County, Ohio, once in the collection of Frederick A. Pfaff. Gift of Mrs. William E. O. Wieneke, 1911.453.

880. **Discoidal,** arkose of angular flint pebbles in a matrix of ferruginous sandstone, diameter 8.9. Source unknown, 1938.4986.

*881. **Discoidal,** arkose of angular cherty pebbles in a matrix of clay or ferruginous sandstone, diameter 8.9. Source unknown, but once in the collection of Dorfeuille's Museum, Cincinnati. Gift of Thomas Cleneay, 1887.12457.

*882. **Projectile Point** related to Cahokia Corner-Notched type, flint, length 7.5. From Alton, Illinois. Gift of Thomas Cleneay, 1887.6514.

883. **Square-Mouth Bowl,** pottery, Neeley's Ferry Plain, height 11.0. From Arkansas Collection of C. W. Riggs. Gift of Dr. S. C. Heighway, 1937.757.

884. **Short-Necked Bottle,** pottery, Bell Plain, height 15.8. From Arkansas collection of C. W. Riggs. Gift of Dr. S. C. Heighway, 1937.709.

885. **Expanded-Center Jar,** pottery, Bell Plain, height 13.7. From Arkansas collection of C. W. Riggs. Gift of Dr. S. C. Heighway, 1937.789.

886. **Bottle with Ogival Strap on Shoulder,** pottery, Bell Plain, height 17.8. From Arkansas collection of C. W. Riggs. Gift of Dr. S. C. Heighway, 1937.786.

887. **Vertical Compound Vessel,** pottery, Bell Plain, height 20.8. From Arkansas collection of C. W. Riggs. Gift of Dr. S. C. Heighway, 1937.664.

888. **Bowl with Crowned Head on Rim,** pottery, Bell Plain, height 14.4. From Arkansas collection of C. W. Riggs. Gift of Dr. S. C. Heighway, 1937.1207.

889. **Tapered-Neck Bottle,** pottery, Bell Plain, distinctive late neck style, height 28.3. From Arkansas collection of C. W. Riggs. Gift of Dr. S. C. Heighway, 1937.875.

*890. **Frog Effigy Jar,** pottery, Bell Plain, height 8.4. From Arkansas collection of C. W. Riggs. Gift of Dr. S. C. Heighway, 1937.1073.

891. **Globular Bottle,** pottery, Bell Plain, side-opening mouth and owl mask on neck, height 10.7. From Arkansas collection of C. W. Riggs. Gift of Dr. S. C. Heighway, 1937.1030.

*892. **Bottle,** pottery, Bell Plain, style of southeast Missouri, height 23.5. From Missouri. Gift of General M. F. Force, 1894.537.

893. **Animal Head Effigy Cup,** pottery, Neeley's Ferry Plain, height 6.0. From Arkansas collection of C. W. Riggs. Gift of Dr. S. C. Heighway, 1937.1015.

894. **Bowl with Bird's Head Projecting Above Rim,** pottery, Neeley's Ferry Plain, height 17.2. From Arkansas collection of C. W. Riggs. Gift of Dr. S. C. Heighway, 1937.911.

895. **Bowl with Two Animal Effigy Handles on Rim,** Neeley's Ferry Plain, pottery, height 12.4. From Arkansas collection of C. W. Riggs. Gift of Dr. S. C. Heighway, 1937.998.

896. **Gourd Bottle with Anthropomorphic mouth,** pottery, Neeley's Ferry Plain, incised cross on bottom, height 11.5. From Arkansas collection of C. W. Riggs. Gift of Dr. S. C. Heighway, 1937.999.

897. **Hunchback Effigy Bottle,** pottery, height 12.8. Found in Mississippi County, Missouri, about 35 miles from Cairo, 1877. Gift of General M. F. Force, 1894.539.

898. **Tripod Bottle,** pottery, St. Francis Plain, short wide neck, globular body, height 19.3. From Arkansas collection of C. W. Riggs. Gift of Dr. S. C. Heighway, 1937.1126.

899. **Bowl with Serpent Head and Coiled Tail on Rim,** pottery, Neeley's Ferry Plain, St. Francis area, height 16.5. From Arkansas collection of C. W. Riggs. Gift of Dr. S. C. Heighway, 1937.693.

*900. **Deep Bowl,** pottery, Neeley's Ferry Plain, one notched and one plain horizontal handle extending from rim, horizontal fins between handles 2.5 below rim, four pairs of lugs between handles and fins 5.0 below rim, height 19.0. From Arkansas collection of C. W. Riggs. Gift of Dr. S. C. Heighway, 1937.1066.

*901. **Bowl,** pottery, Parkin Punctate body, Barton Incised rim, late style of southwest Tennessee near Memphis, height 10.2. From Arkansas collection of C. W. Riggs. Gift of Dr. S. C. Heighway, 1937.848.

*902. **Bowl,** pottery, Barton incised neck, plain body, two false handles on opposite sides of rim with two applied masks between, notched lip, late, about A.D. 1500-1600, height 7.8. From Arkansas collection of C. W. Riggs. Gift of Dr. S. C. Heighway, 1937.917.

*903. **Bowl with Wide Outflaring Lip,** pottery, Rhodes Incised, underside of lip vertically ribbed, body incised with four connected swastika-spirals with small swastika-spirals in spandrels on shoulder, height 11.8, about A.D. 1500-1600. From Arkansas collection of C. W. Riggs. Gift of Dr. S. C. Heighway, 1937.1070.

*904. **Bottle,** pottery, Rhodes Incised, short wide neck, swastika-spirals on body, small swastika spirals in circles on shoulder between body spirals, height 20.0. From Arkansas collection of C. W. Riggs. Gift of Dr. S. C. Heighway, 1937.994.

*905. **Vertical Compound Vessel,** pottery, Fortune Noded, height 15.5. From Arkansas collection of C. W. Riggs. Gift of Dr. S. C. Heighway, 1937.961.

906. **Bowl with Pierced, Flanged Lip,** pottery, probably Bell Plain, height 13.2. From Arkansas. Gift of C. W. Riggs, 1889.618.

*907. **Jar with Wide Neck,** pottery, Walls Engraved, neck plain, body decorated with vertical crosshatched bands alternating with plain bands, height 18.5. From Arkansas collection of C. W. Riggs. Gift of Dr. S. C. Heighway, 1937.988.

908. **Long Necked Bottle,** pottery, Caddoan undecorated type, fine-grained, dark brown paste, somewhat burnished surface, height 29.0. From Missouri. Gift of Thomas Cleneay, 1887.20897.

909. **Deep Bowl,** pottery, Old Town Red, four applied masks just under lip instead of handles, red-slipped inside and out, height 19.8. From Arkansas collection of C. W. Riggs. Gift of Dr. S. C. Heighway, 1937.957.

*910. **Tripod Bottle,** pottery, Old Town Red, globular body with offset shoulder, short fairly narrow neck, red slip inside and out, height 27.5. From Arkansas collection of C. W. Riggs. Gift of Dr. S. C. Heighway, 1937.990.

911. **Jar,** pottery, Nodena Red and White, short, wide neck slip-painted red, red and white vertical stripes on body contracting to red foot, height 15.6. From the Arkansas collection of C. W. Riggs. Gift of Dr. S. C. Heighway, 1937.992.

*912. **Bottle,** pottery, Nodena Red and White, wide, medium-tall neck, flattened globular body, deep foot, red swastika-spirals on body radiating from center white circle, additional spirals on neck, slipped on outside only, height 23.5. From Arkansas collection of C. W. Riggs. Gift of Dr. S. C. Heighway, 1937.991.

*913. **Bottle,** pottery, Avenue Polychrome, short, wide neck slip-painted red inside and out, body decorated with four simple reversing red and white spirals with vestiges of a darker color between, height 18.5. From Arkansas collection of C. W. Riggs. Gift of Dr. S. C. Heighway, 1937.996.

914. **Jar, pottery,** Carson Red on Buff, short wide neck, red filmed inside and out except for band around middle of neck left buff and punctated, globular body red-filmed, height 19.2. From Arkansas collection of C. W. Riggs. Gift of Dr. S. C. Heighway, 1937.665.

915. **Shallow Bowl,** pottery, Carson Red on Buff, red slip-painted swastika spiral from center bottom to lip inside and out, height 6.2. From Arkansas collection of C. W. Riggs. Gift of Dr. S. C. Heighway, 1937.1028.

*916. **Bottle,** pottery, Carson Red on Buff, short wide neck, horizontal band of red at lip and halfway down neck, four wide, vertical red bands on body, well-defined slightly concave bottom, height 16.5. From Arkansas collection of C. W. Riggs. Gift of Dr. S. C. Heighway, 1937.995.

*917. **Elbow Pipe,** pottery of late Arkansas type, 7.6 by 6.3. Source unknown. Gift of Thomas Cleneay, 1887.20913.

918. **Projectile Points,** flint, lower Arkansas River type, ovoid or bay-leaf shape, length 4.0-5.3, about A.D. 1600. Source unknown, 1938.5262, .5265, .5266, .5276, .5282.

919. **Shell Pendant,** cut from shell, probably of a freshwater bivalve, length 11.0. From Arkansas. Gift of C. W. Riggs, 1889.868.

Madisonville — Fort Ancient

*920. **Pedestal Jar,** pottery, Madisonville Cordmarked, height 19.6, diameter of bowl. 15.6, probably datable about A.D. 1400-1600. Excavated October 7, 1879, at the Madisonville, Ohio, site under the direction of Dr. Charles L. Metz. Gift of Judge Joseph Cox, 1888.715. Said to be the only pedestal vessel found in North American in a pre-European context with the exception of the bowl of another one, minus the pedestal, found near this one and also in Cincinnati Art Museum. Illustrated in Low Notebook,** p. 31. Published: Low, "Archaeological Explorations," 1880, Pt. II, pp. 132-133, fig. 26; Moorehead, *Stone Age,* 1910, Vol. II, fig. 663, p. 270; Willoughby, *Madisonville,* 1920, pl. 24-k; *Bulletin C.A.M.,* Jan., 1939, p. 6; Griffin, *Fort Ancient,* 1943, p. 137, Table V-11, pl. LXVI-4.

*921. **Jar with Applied Salamanders,** pottery, Madisonville Cordmarked, height 15.3. From Madisonville site. Gift of Judge Joseph Cox, 1888.714. Published: Low, "Archaeological Ex-

**List of abbreviated references follows end of Catalogue Listing.*

plorations," 1880, Pt. III, p. 216, fig. 38; Moorehead, *Stone Age,* 1910, Vol. II, fig. 662, p. 269; *Bulletin C.A.M.,* Jan. 1939, p. 6; Griffin, *Fort Ancient,* 1943, pp. 135-136, Table V-1, pl. LXVI-3.

922. **Vertical Compound Vessel,** pottery, Madisonville Plain, height 12.1. Excavated March, 1879, at Madisonville site under the direction of Dr. Charles L. Metz, once in the collection of W. C. Rogers, Madisonville. Gift of Dr. S. C. Heighway, 1937.962. Illustrated in Low Notebook, p. 27. Published: Short, *North Americans of Antiquity,* 1880, p. 527; Low, "Archaeological Explorations," 1880, Pt. I, p. 46; Griffin, *Fort Ancient,* 1943, pl. LXVI-1.

*923. **Jar,** pottery, Madisonville Plain, a single line of punctations on shoulder, height 13.5. From the Madisonville site. Gift of Judge Joseph Cox through the Women's Art Museum Association, 1881.1. Published: Griffin, *Fort Ancient,* 1943, Table III-45.

*924. **Bowl,** pottery, Madisonville Cordmarked, four handles, notched lip, height 13.7. From the Madisonville site. Gift of Judge Joseph Cox through the Women's Art Museum Association, 1881.3.

*925. **Jar,** pottery, Madisonville Grooved Paddle, no handles, pair of holes just below lip, height 11.0 Excavated July 9, 1879, at Madisonville site under the direction of Dr. Metz. Gift of Judge Joseph Cox, 1888.698. Published: Low, "Archaeological Explorations," 1880, Pt. I, fig. 17, p. 61; Griffin, *Fort Ancient,* 1943, pl. LXVI-6.

*926. **Pipe Bowl in The Form of a Human Face marked with the Weeping Eye,** probably fine-grained sandstone, height 4.4. Source unknown, 1938.5178.

927. **Pipe Bowl in the Form of an Animal Head,** shale, height 5.3. Source unknown. Gift of Thomas Cleneay, 1887.20681.

*928. **Pipe Bowl in the Shape of a Vase,** probably limestone, height 4.7. Excavated March 28, 1879, at Madisonville site under direction of Dr. Metz; part of the R. O. Collis collection of finds from the Madisonville site, deposited in the Cincinnati Art Museum in 1888 by Dr. Metz and purchased for the Museum by Harry Levy, 1908.1015. Illustrated in Low Notebook, p. 26. Published: Low, "Archaeological Explorations," 1880, Pt. I, fig. 4, p. 46.

929. **Pipe Bowl in the Form of an Animal Head,** limestone with the surface partly dissolved by water action, length 7.0. Excavated April 2, 1879, at Madisonville site by Dr. Metz. Gift of Judge

Joseph Cox, 1888.492. Illustrated in Low Notebook, pp. 28, 56. Published: Low, "Archaeological Explorations," 1880, Pt. I, p. 48.

930. **Elbow Pipe,** probably red Ohio pipestone, flaring rim, incised triangles on bottom and sides, weeping eye motif incised on top of stem centered on a hole, length 6.0. Excavated at Madisonville site May 7, 1879, under the direction of Dr. Metz; part of the R. O. Collis collection of finds from the Madisonville site, deposited in the Cincinnati Art Museum in 1888 by Dr. Metz and purchased for the Museum by Harry Levy, 1908.1017. Illustrated in Low Notebook, p. 28. Published: Low, "Archaeological Explorations," 1880, Pt. I, fig. 11, p. 53.

931. **Pipe Bowl Incised on Both Sides with Design of Bird with Outstretched Wings,** fine-grained muddy sandstone, height 4.9. Surface find at Madisonville site, May 1, 1880. Donor unknown, 1938.5016. Published: Low, "Archaeological Explorations," 1880, Pt. III, p. 213, fig. 35; Willoughby, *Madisonville,* 1920, p. 73, pl. 19-b.

*932. **Hemispherical Pipe Bowl with Notched Ridges,** shale or fine-grained sandstone, diameter about 5.0. Excavated April 13, 1888, at Madisonville site under direction of Dr. Metz. Gift of Harry Zerring, 1918.846. Published: Low, "Archaeological Explorations," 1880, Pt. I, p. 46, fig. 34.

*933. **Pipe Bowl in the Form of a Long-Beaked Bird,** sandstone, height 6.5. Source unknown, 1938.5143.

934. **Discoidal,** cordmarked, shell tempered pottery, pierced in the center, diameter 6.0. Source unknown, 1938.4190.

935. **Discoidal,** quartzite, slightly biconcave, not pierced, diameter 6.5. Source unknown, but once in Dorfeuille's Museum, Cincinnati. Gift of Thomas Cleneay, 1887.12456.

936. **Discoidal,** quartzite, biconcave, not pierced, diameter 6.7. Source unknown, but once in Dorfeuille's Museum, Cincinnati. Gift of Thomas Cleneay, 1887.12450.

937. **Discoidal,** sandstone, a cross incised on each flat face, diameter 3.3. Source unknown, 1938.2742.

938. **Discoidal,** shaly sandstone, biconcave, pierced, incised shallow lines radiating from center hole, diameter 5.5. From Clermont County, Ohio. Gift of Thomas Cleneay, 1887.11434.

939. **Discoidal,** shaly sandstone, biconcave, pierced, lenticular shape incised on one side,

tangents to center hole incised on the other, diameter 5.9. From Clermont County, Ohio. Gift of Thomas Cleneay, 1887.11435.

940. **Triangular Arrowhead,** flint, length 6.2. Source unknown. Gift of Thomas Cleneay, 1887.18730.

941. **Triangular Arrowhead,** flint, length 4.3. Source unknown; once in the collection of R. K. Crane. Gift of Thomas Cleneay, 1887.17777.

942. **Triangular Arrowhead,** flint, length 3.9. From Alton, Illinois. Gift of Thomas Cleneay, 1887.6472.

*943-952. **Triangular Arrowheads,** flint, length 2.6-4.9. From Boone County, Kentucky. Gift of Thomas Cleneay, 1887.5604, .5626, .5635, .5650, .5665, .5516, .5634, .5627, .5664, .5617.

*953-958. **Triangular Arrowheads,** flint, length 3.8-4.9. Source unknown, 1938.1157, .3906, .3904, .3900, .3907, .8119.

959-960. **Triangular Arrowheads,** flint, length 4.3-4.6. From Ohio River bank opposite Aurora, Indiana. Gift of Thomas Cleneay, 1887.7508, .7690.

961. **Triangular Arrowhead,** flint probably from Flint Ridge, Ohio, length 4.1. From Boone County, Kentucky. Gift of Thomas Cleneay, 1887.5619.

962. **Triangular Serrated Arrowhead,** flint, length 3.4 Source unknown. Gift of Thomas Cleneay, 1887.17711.

963. **Triangular Serrated Arrowhead,** flint, length 4.6. Source unknown, 1938.4031.

964. **Side-Notched Arrowhead,** flint, length 3.8. From Alton, Illinois. Gift of Thomas Cleneay, 1887.6453.

965. **Triangular Arrowhead Converted to a Drill,** flint, length 3.5. From Boone County, Kentucky. Gift of Thomas Cleneay, 1887.5641.

*966. **Celt** chipped bedded flint or novaculite, ground and polished edge, length 20.5. From the mouth of the Big Miami River. Gift of Thomas Cleneay, 1887.6892.

967. **Scraper,** flint, length 3.7, Madisonville type. From Kentucky. Gift of Thomas Cleneay, 1887.12103.

968. **Spoon or Scoop,** shell of freshwater clam, length 17.6. Source unknown, but vicinity of Cincinnati. Gift of Judge Joseph Cox, 1888.507.

*969. **Hoe Blade,** shell of freshwater clam, pierced for attachment, length 13.0. Source unknown, but vicinity of Cincinnati. Gift of Judge Joseph Cox, 1888.510.

*970. **Spoon with Serrated Edge,** shell of freshwater clam, length 11.5, one end cut as a stepped thumbpiece and pierced, decorated with lines and clusters of circular pits. Excavated August, 1879, in a pottery vessel, at the Madisonville site under the direction of Dr. Metz. Gift of Harry Zerring, 1918.803. Illustrated in Low Notebook, p. 26. Published: Low, "Archaeological Explorations," 1880, Pt. I, p. 64, fig. 21; Holmes, "Art in Shell," 1880-81, fig. 4; Fowke, 1902, pp. 685-6, fig. 277; Willoughby, *Madisonville*, 1920, p. 66.

971. **Cylindrical Drill,** flint, chipped on all edges and ground on basal edge, length 6.4. From Bourbon County, Kentucky. Gift of Thomas Cleneay, 1887.14234.

*972 **Cylindrical Drill,** flint, length 9.4. From Butler County, Ohio. Gift of Thomas Cleneay, 1887.18372.

973. **Cylindrical Drill,** flint, length 8.3. Source unknown but once in Crockett collection, Portsmouth, Ohio. Gift of Thomas Cleneay, 1887.18711.

974-975. **Cylindrical Drills,** flint, chipped on all edges, length 10.4, 6.0. Source unknown. Gift of Thomas Cleneay, 1887.16727, .18712.

*976. **Cylindrical Drill,** flint, length 6.7. Source unknown, 1938.3666.

977. **Cylindrical Drill,** flint, length 5.7. Cleneay's notation says, "Aurora, Indiana, bought of a merchant." Gift of Thomas Cleneay, 1887.13889.

*978. **Pendants,** (a) slate, (b, c) cannel coal, length 2.0-3.7. From Athens County, Ohio. Gift of Thomas Cleneay, 1887.15431.

979. **Claw-Shaped Pendant,** cannel coal, length 3.2. Source unknown, 1938.2995.

980. **Claw-Shaped Pendant,** cannel coal, length 3.5. From area of Gallipolis, Ohio, Point Pleasant, West Virginia. Gift of Thomas Cleneay, 1887.14658.

*981. **Claw-Shaped Pendant,** cannel coal, straight portion marked with three circular pits and a transverse groove, length 5.7. From Ohio River valley opposite Chilo, Ohio. Gift of Thomas Cleneay, 1887.14703.

982. **Pendant,** cannel coal, length 4.5. Source unknown, 1938.2914.

*983. **Bell,** copper of European manufacture, length 2.6. Excavated September 25, 1879, at Madisonville site under direction of Dr. Metz. Gift of Thomas Cleneay, 1887.20658. Illustrated in Low Notebook, p. 32. Published: Low, "Archaeological Explorations," 1880, Pt. II, p. 131.

*984. **Animal Head Pendant,** bone, length 5.0. From the R. O. Collis collection of finds from the Madisonville site, deposited in the Cincinnati Art Museum in 1888 by Dr. Metz and purchased for the Museum by Harry Levy, 1908.271. Illustrated in Low Notebook, p. 17.

985. **Cylindrical Beads,** 157 strung together, bone, largest about 2.0 long. From Blennerhasset Island in the Ohio River. Gift of Thomas Cleneay, 1887.20632.

986. **Cylindrical Beads,** bone, length about 4.5. From Powhatan, Ohio. Gift of Thomas Cleneay, 1887.18317 a, b.

987-990. **Cylindrical Beads,** bone, length 5.4-6.4. From the vicinity of Cincinnati. Gift of Judge Joseph Cox, 1888.341, .358-360.

991-992. **Cylindrical Beads,** bone, length 3.0-3.5. From the R. O. Collis collection of finds from the Madisonville site, deposited in the Cincinnati Art Museum in 1888 by Dr. Metz and purchased for the Museum by Harry Levy, 1908.436, .438.

*993-994. **Bear's Teeth for Pendants,** length 4.3, 4.5. Source unknown, 1938.4299-4300.

995-999. **Shell Disks,** diameter 1.7-3.0. From the R. O. Collis collection of finds from the Madisonville site, deposited in the Museum in 1888 by Dr. Metz and purchased for the Museum by Harry Levy, 1908.207-209, .212, .214.

*1000. **Awl,** turkey bone, notched margins and row of decorative pits at broad end, length 10.6. From the vicinity of Cincinnati. Gift of Judge Joseph Cox, 1888.431.

1001. **Awl,** bone, length 6.7. Source unknown, 1938.3384.

1002. **Awl or Pin,** bone, length 6.5. From the Low collection, Madisonville. Gift of Harry Zerring, 1918.3455.

1003. **Awl or Pin,** bone, length 6.4. Source unknown, 1938.5147.

*1004. **Awl,** bone, length 14.6. Source unknown, 1938.5152.

*1005. **Awl,** elk bone, length 13.4. Source unknown, but collected by Cincinnati Art Museum members in Ohio River valley, 1918.5862.

1006. **Needle,** bone, length 4.4. Source unknown, 1938.5150.

*1007-1009. **Flaking Tools,** sections of deer antler, length about 3.5. From the R. O. Collis collection of finds from the Madisonville site, deposited in the Cincinnati Art Museum in 1888 by Dr. Metz and purchased for the Museum by Harry Levy, 1908.272, .275, .294.

*1010. **Fishhook,** bone, length 4.4. From the vicinity of Cincinnati. Gift of Judge Joseph Cox, 1888.480.

1011. **Fishhook,** bone, length 5.1. Source unknown, 1938.4995.

*1012. **Harpoon,** deer antler, length 24.4. From the vicinity of Cincinnati. Gift of Judge Joseph Cox, 1888.426.

1013. **Awl,** bird bone, length 16.7. From the vicinity of Cincinnati. Gift of Judge Joseph Cox, 1888.442.

1014. **Sinew Stone,** sandstone, for grinding down arrow shafts, etc., length about 6.5. Source unknown, 1938.3004.

*1015. **Hoe Blade,** deer antler, length 20.0. Source unknown. Gift of Dr. S. C. Heighway, 1937.7306.

*1016. **Spatula,** deer antler, possibly for working pottery, length 19.8. From the R. O. Collis collection of finds from Madisonville site, deposited in the Cincinnati Art Museum in 1888 by Dr. Metz and purchased for the Museum by Harry Levy, 1908.505.

1017. **Pick,** deer antler tine, length 27.3. From the R. O. Collis collection of finds from the Madisonville site, deposited in the Cincinnati Art Museum in 1888 by Dr. Metz and purchased for the Museum by Harry Levy, 1908.1180.

*1018. **Arrow-Shaft Straightener,** antler, length 10.4. Source unknown, 1938.5134.

*1019-1021. **Arrowheads,** antler tips, length 5.3-6.1. From the Low collection, Madisonville. Gift of Harry Zerring, 1918.3514, .3533, .3576.

1022. **Arrowhead,** antler tip, length 5.2, pierced. Source unknown, 1938.4297.

*1023. **Flute,** bird bone, six holes still intact, possibly three more originally, length 11.3. Source unknown, but probably Madisonville. Gift of Harry Zerring, 1918.834.

*1024. **Rasp,** rib-bone, length 21.2. Source unknown, but probably Madisonville. Gift of Harry Zerring, 1918.3877.

1025. **Fragment of a Rasp,** rib-bone, length 10.5. From the vicinity of Cincinnati. Gift of Judge Joseph Cox, 1888.419.

*1026. **Scraper,** deer jaw, length 21.0. From Sand Hill, Hamilton County, Ohio. Gift of Harry Zerring, 1918.4710.

*1027. **Beamer,** bone, length 26.2, probably used for dressing hides. From the R. O. Collis collection of finds from the Madisonville site, deposited in the Cincinnati Art Museum in 1888 by Dr. Metz and purchased for the Museum by Harry Levy, 1908.535.

1028. **Disk Pendants,** shell, diameter about 4.2. From the vicinity of Cincinnati. Gift of Judge Joseph Cox, 1888.498-499.

1029. **Disk Pendant,** shell, diameter about 5.6. Source unknown, but probably Madisonville. Gift of Harry Zerring, 1918.826.

1030. **Cylindrical Pendant,** cut from columella of Busycon shell, length 6.5, grooved at one end to make a neck. Source unknown, 1938.4990.

1031. **Spoon-Shaped Pendant,** shell, length 2.7. Source unknown, but probably Madisonville. Gift of Harry Zerring, 1918.830.

1032. **Cylindrical Beads,** cut from columella of Busycon shell, length about 2.5-5.0. From the Low collection, Madisonville. Gift of Harry Zerring, 1918.3365.

1033. **Bone Tubular Beads and Canine Pendants,** length about 3.0-5.0. From West Virginia. Gift of Thomas Cleneay, 1887.15527.

Late Additions to the Exhibition

The Southwest

1034. **Jar,** slip painted pottery, height 28.5. From Acoma Pueblo, XIX c., collected by J. M. Stevenson, Bureau of Ethnology number 110007. Gift of the Women's Art Museum Association (from the U. S. National Museum in trade for Rookwood pottery), 1885.46.

1035. **Bowl,** slip painted pottery, height 14.0. From New Mexico, probably Acoma Pueblo. Gift of the Women's Art Museum Association (from the U. S. National Museum), 1885.58.

1036. **Figure of a Man,** slip painted pottery, height 53.3. From New Mexico, collected in Zuni early XX c., but probably made in Cochiti. Gift of Mary Hanna, 1915.45.

1037. **Rug,** wool, 191.0 by 134.0. Red ground, stripes of black-brown, natural white and white, gray and black-brown diamonds. Navajo tribe, XIX c. Gift of Amelia Elizabeth White, 1937.570.

1038. **Rug** in style of a Third Phase Chief's Blanket, wool, 157.0 by 278.0. Black and natural white stripes, central stripe red and purple, striped lozenges of purple, red and white in corners and center. Navajo tribe, XIX-XX c. Bequest of Ruth Harrison, 1940.705.

1039. **Blanket,** wool, 180.0 by 112.0. Stripes of brown and of red with diamonds of navy and natural white rectangles. Navajo tribe, XIX-XX c. Gift of Amelia Elizabeth White, 1937.391.

The Plains

1040. **Standard,** calico casing with eagle wing-feather fringe and squirrel fur, length 180.9. Cheyenne tribe, Wyoming, XIX c. Gift of General M. F. Force, 1894.96.

Abbreviated References

Bulletin C.A.M., 1939 = *Bulletin of the Cincinnati Art Museum,* January 1939

Fowke, 1902 = Gerard Fowke, *Archaeological History of Ohio,* Columbus, Ohio, Ohio State Archaeological and Historical Society, 1902

Griffin, *Fort Ancient,* 1943 = J. B. Griffin, *The Fort Ancient Aspect,* Ann Arbor, University of Michigan, 1943

Holmes, "Art in Shell" = William H. Holmes, "Art in Shell of the Ancient Americans," *Second Annual Report of the Bureau of Ethnology to the Secretary of the Smithsonian Institution, 1880-81,* Washington, 1883

Low Notebook = unpublished notebook prepared by Charles F. Low with sketches, diagrams and photographs of excavations in the Cincinnati area around 1880 and objects found by him, Dr. Metz, and others at Madisonville and other archaeological sites in southern Ohio

Low, "Archaeological Explorations," 1880 = Charles F. Low, "Archaeological Explorations near Madisonville, Ohio," *Journal of the Cincinnati Society of Natural History,* Vol. III, no 1, May 1880, Vol. III, no. 2, July 1880, Vol. III, no. 3, October 1880

Moorehead, *Stone Age,* 1910 = Warren K. Moorehead, *The Stone Age in North America,* Boston and New York, Houghton Mifflin, 1910

Short, 1880 = John Short, *North Americans of Antiquity,* New York, Harper, 1880

Willoughby, *Madisonville,* 1920 = Earnest A. Hooten with notes on the artifacts by Charles C. Willoughby, *Papers of the Peabody Museum of American Archaeology and Ethnology,* Harvard University, Vol. VIII, no. 1, Indian Village Site and Cemetery near Madisonville, Ohio, Cambridge, 1920

Cover illustration: 158. Painted Buffalo Hide.

Botanical Identification of Basket Fibers

Willow, *salix*
Sedge grass, *carex barbarae*
Redbud, *cercis occidentalis*
Bulrush, *scirpus pacificus*
Maidenhair fern, *adiatum pedatum, adiantum pedatum*
Hazelnut, *corylus californica*
Sourgrass or Squawgrass, *xerophyllum tenax*
Giant chain fern, *woodwardia spinulosa*
Devil's claw, *martynia frangrans*
Cattail, *typha augustifolia*
Sumac, *rhus trilobata*
Mountain mahogany, *cercocarpus betulifolius*
Indian hemp, *apocynum cannabinum*
Cane, *arundinaria tecta*
Cladium, *cladium mariscus*
Rush, *juncus acutus, balticus, effusus, textilis*
Western juniper, *juniperus occidentalis*
Reed, *phragmites phragmites*
Bracken, *pteridium aguilinum*
Tule, *scirpus lacustris*
Yucca, *yucca glauca*

Typesetting, Craftsman Type Inc.; lithography, Young and Klein, Inc.; design and typography, Noel Martin; photography, F. V. Raymond, Dutro Blocksom, Ron Forth, Greg Grosse, Danny Daniels.